ATTRIBUTE GAMES AND ACTIVITIES
Maria Marolda

Creative Publications

ACKNOWLEDGMENT
To the set of people who have
been and are very special to me . . .
AJM, ARR, FMR, DAR, RMM, PSD,
and of course, Matthew.

ISBN: 0-88488-052-4
Printed in the U.S.A.

©1976 Creative Publications
788 Palomar Avenue
Sunnyvale, CA 94086
Printed in U.S.A.

12 . 898

TABLE OF CONTENTS

Title	Concept Being Presented	Page
Introduction		7
ATTRIBUTE BLOCKS		11
Sorting Activity	Classification	13
Finding Subsets	Classification	14
"Not" Sets	Negations	15
Name the Set	Classification	16
Matching Activity	Classification	17
Concentration Game	Classification	18
Attribute Card Game	Classification	19
Arranging Game	Logical Thinking	20
Someone Else's Arrangement (SAP)†	Logical Thinking	21
Twenty Questions Game	Logical Thinking	22
An Example of Twenty Questions Game	Logical Thinking	23
Who Am I? Game	Logical Thinking	24
In the Loop	Logical Thinking	25
Sorting According to Differences and Similarities	Logical Thinking	26
Difference Activity (SAP)	Logical Thinking	27
Follow the Arrows (SAP)	Logical Thinking	28
A Difference Activity (SAP)	Logical Thinking	29
Making Chains and Trains	Logical Thinking	30
A Difference Train (SAP)	Logical Thinking	31
A Three Difference Train (SAP)	Logical Thinking	32
Making Other Arrangements	Logical Thinking	33
2 x 2 Arranging Mat (SAP)	Logical Thinking	34
The "H" Mat (SAP)	Logical Thinking	35
What Is Missing in the Two-Difference "H"? (SAP)	Logical Thinking	36
3 x 3 Arranging Mat (SAP)	Logical Thinking	37
What Is Missing in the Square? (SAP)	Logical Thinking	38
4 x 4 Arranging Mat (SAP)	Logical Thinking	39
What Is Missing in the Square? (SAP)	Logical Thinking	40
Watch It! Game	Logical Thinking	41
Watch It! Game Mat (SAP)	Logical Thinking	42
Difference Game	Logical Thinking	43
Difference Game Mat (SAP)	Logical Thinking	44
Two-Loop Problems	Unions and Intersections	45
More Two-Loop Problems	Unions and Intersections	46

†SAP indicates Student Activity Page

3

Two-Loop Activity	Unions and Intersections	47
Unions and Intersections	Unions and Intersections	48
Intersection Game	Unions and Intersections	49
In the Loops	Unions and Intersections	50
What's Missing? Game	Unions and Intersections	51
Match Game	Unions and Intersections	52
Three-Loop Problems	Unions and Intersections	53
Three-Loop Games	Unions and Intersections	54
Be a Detective (SAP)	Logical Thinking	55
Detective Questions (SAP)	Logical Thinking	56
PEOPLE PIECES		57
Finding Subsets	Classification	59
Arranging the Tiles Game	Classification	60
Someone Else's Arrangement (SAP)	Logical Thinking	61
Name the Set	Classification	62
Concentration Game	Classification	63
Finding Differences and Similarities	Logical Thinking	64
Special Arrangements	Logical Thinking	65
Special Arrangements (SAP)	Logical Thinking	66
Alike/Difference Sorting	Logical Thinking	67
Alike/Difference Sorting Mat (SAP)	Logical Thinking	68
Two-Loop Problems	Unions and Intersections	69
More Two-Loop Problems	Unions and Intersections	70
Two-Loop Activity	Unions and Intersections	71
Unions and Intersections	Unions and Intersections	72
What's Missing? Game	Unions and Intersections	73
Missing Persons	Logical Thinking	74
Three-Loop Problems	Unions and Intersections	75
Three-Loop Challenge Game	Unions and Intersections	76
COLOR CUBES		77
Making and Copying Designs	Intuitive Geometry	79
Color Cube Graph Paper, 6x6 (SAP)	Intuitive Geometry	80
Color Cube Graph Paper, 10x10 (SAP)	Intuitive Geometry	81
Pattern Page 1 (SAP)	Intuitive Geometry	82
Pattern Page 2 (SAP)	Intuitive Geometry	83
Pattern Page 3 (SAP)	Intuitive Geometry	84
Pattern Page 4 (SAP)	Intuitive Geometry	85
Pattern Page 5 (SAP)	Intuitive Geometry	86
Pattern Page 6 (SAP)	Intuitive Geometry	87
Pattern Page 7 (SAP)	Intuitive Geometry	88
Pattern Page 8 (SAP)	Intuitive Geometry	89
Repeating Designs	Intuitive Geometry	90
Repeating a Design (SAP)	Intuitive Geometry	91

Arranging the Cubes (SAP)	Intuitive Geometry	92
Someone Else's Pattern (SAP)	Intuitive Geometry	93
Another Repeating Design (SAP)	Intuitive Geometry	94
Repeating Design—3 (SAP)	Intuitive Geometry	95
Mirror Designs	Symmetry	96
An Example of Symmetric Design (SAP)	Symmetry	97
Subsets of Cubes	Subsets	98
More Subsets	Permutations and Combinations	99
How Many Ways?	Permutations and Combinations	100
Four in a Row Game	Logical Thinking	101
Moving Pairs of Cubes	Transformations	102
Pattern Page 9 (SAP)	Transformations	103
Rotating Logs	Transformations	104
More Moves	Transformations	105
Flipping Logs	Transformations	106
Flipping Groups of Cubes	Transformations	107
More Flips	Transformations	108
Combining Moves	Transformations	109
EXTENSIONS TO NUMBERS		111
Arranging the Numerals	Number Patterns	113
Hundred Chart (SAP)	Number Patterns	114
Hundred Mat (SAP)	Number Patterns	115
5 x 10 Arrangement Mat (SAP)	Number Patterns	116
3 x 10 Arrangement Mat (SAP)	Number Patterns	117
Another Arrangement (SAP)	Number Patterns	118
Arranging the Tiles (SAP)	Number Patterns	119
A Different Arrangement (SAP)	Number Patterns	120
Challenge Arrangement (SAP)	Number Patterns	121
Sorting the Numerals	Number Patterns	122
Finding Multiples	Multiples and Factors	123
Common Multiples	Multiples and Factors	124
Multiples of 2 and 7 (SAP)	Multiples and Factors	125
Making Windows	Multiples and Factors	126
2-Window (SAP)	Multiples and Factors	127
3-Window (SAP)	Multiples and Factors	128
5-Window (SAP)	Multiples and Factors	129
7-Window (SAP)	Multiples and Factors	130
Investigating Window Patterns	Multiples and Factors	131
Covering the Chart	Multiples and Factors	132
Common Factors	Multiples and Factors	133
Prime Numbers	Multiples and Factors	134
Finding the Least Common Multiple and the Greatest Common Factor Using Loops	Multiples and Factors	135

Finding LCM and GCF (SAP)   Multiples and Factors   136
More LCM's and GCF's (SAP)   Multiples and Factors   138
Problems to Solve (SAP)   Logical Thinking   140
APPENDIX   143
How to Make Attribute Game Cards   144
Solutions   145

INTRODUCTION

ATTRIBUTE GAMES AND ACTIVITIES is a book for teachers suggesting student experiences with the Attribute Materials. Introductory group activities, games and Student Activity Pages are provided to develop many important mathematical concepts. In a separate packet included with this book is a set of Loop Activity Cards. The physical materials, originally developed by the Elementary Science Study (ESS), consist of *Attribute Blocks,* wooden blocks of four shapes, four colors and two sizes; *People Pieces,* plastic tiles which picture people with the attributes of age, girth, sex and color of clothing; and *Color Cubes,* wooden cubes in six colors.

Mathematical Development

The Attribute Materials may be used to develop many mathematical concepts, including:

Set Theory:	sets, subsets, negations, union, intersection and Venn diagrams
Geometry:	basic shapes, symmetry, transformations, and intuitive concepts
Number Theory:	sequences, permutations, combinations, factors, multiples, common factors, common multiples, least common multiples and greatest common factors
Logical Thinking:	finding patterns and solving problems with Venn diagrams

The concept toward which each page is directed is identified in the Table of Contents.

Learning Stages

ATTRIBUTE GAMES AND ACTIVITIES is designed according to learning stages such as those defined by Piaget. The activities may be used at four stages:

Concrete Stage:	The physical materials are used according to verbal directions. The materials are placed directly on the pages and students manipulate the materials to do all the work. Students may respond by manipulating the materials.
Semi-concrete Stage:	The directions are given through pictorial presentations, such as Student Activity Pages. The physical materials are selected according to pictorial cues, and work is done by manipulating the materials. Students respond by drawing pictures of the results.
Semi-abstract Stage:	The directions are given through pictorial presentations. Students think through problems, referring to the physical materials, but not actually manipulating them. Students respond by drawing pictures of the results.
Abstract Stage:	The directions are given with coded symbols to represent the physical materials. Students think through the problem situations without actually manipulating physical materials. Students respond with coded symbols.

Since these learning stages are *implicit* in the development of the specific activities, the teacher may adapt the same activity to a variety of stages.

Use of the Book

The introductory group activities, games and Student Activity Pages are intended to provide a variety of experiences which may be used in many ways.

Introductory group activities are designed to be led by a teacher, but can later be led by a student.

Games may be used for motivation or practice of specific math concepts.

Student Activity Pages follow many of the introductory group activities and are used to extend or apply the concept being studied. The Student Activity Pages are written directly to the student. They are self-explanatory and may be used independently by the student.

7

The experiences may take place in a variety of settings.

In a **regular classroom** with the teacher acting as leader of the experiences.

In **small groups** within a classroom with a teacher, aide or student acting as leader. The groups may work independently of each other according to their needs and interests.

In an **individualized setting** with each student working independently.

In a **mathematics laboratory** where the students work from the Student Activity Pages independently, in pairs or in small groups.

Although the book is intended primarily for teachers, the reading style and level are appropriate for upper elementary students. The teacher role could be assumed by a student leader.

All pages in *ATTRIBUTE GAMES AND ACTIVITIES* are reproducible, so multiple copies may be made and distributed to the students.

Student responses may be elicited in several forms.
1. The students may respond orally to a teacher or student leader.
2. The students may show the arrangement of physical materials to a teacher or fellow student.
3. If the students are working independently, they may record the results by drawing pictures, using magic markers, drawing outlines of the materials with a pencil, or by using a template.

4. At a higher level, students may record their results by using coded symbols. In this case, ⟨b⟩ represents a small, blue diamond.

Sequencing the Activities
The activities are organized into four sections: *Attribute Blocks, People Pieces, Color Cubes* and *Extensions to Numbers*.

Various approaches to a single concept are provided. Since many of the activities described for use with Attribute Blocks are equally appropriate for People Pieces, a concept may be spiraled during the year and from year to year without students repeating exactly the same experience. The materials also provide the opportunity for the teacher to diagnose a level of ability or evaluate a particular concept with a material different from the one used to teach or practice the concept.

Alternately, a concept may be developed through each of the models before going on to another concept. This may be done by the teacher extracting similar activities with each of the four materials and presenting them together to intensively explore a particular concept.

Finally, a particular section or activity may be extracted and used independently of the other sections as an enrichment activity for particular groups of students.

Age Adaptations
ATTRIBUTE GAMES AND ACTIVITIES may be used with both elementary and secondary students. Younger students should be involved at the concrete and semi-concrete levels; their responses being made by showing the physical materials or drawing pictures. For these students, it is advised that the Student Activity Pages be presented in color. To introduce color to the pages, the younger student could actually color the pages before proceeding to the experience described. Color helps the student associate the physical material with its pictorial counterpart and acts as a motivating device. Older students should have experiences manipulating the physical materials, but should proceed more quickly to the semi-abstract and abstract levels. Both directions and student responses should involve the use of coding.

Specific Features of ATTRIBUTE GAMES AND ACTIVITIES

Materials to be used.

Procedure or rules of the game is directed to the teacher. However, it may be included for students' use when a student acts as leader or when the rules for a game must be available.

Further Teaching Suggestions provide pedagogical suggestions, variations which parallel the experience, follow-up activities which extend the experience or challenges which provide more difficult situations based on the same activity. These suggestions should help the teacher adapt the activities for individual differences or adapt the activities for further practice.

```
                         TITLE

    Materials:
    Procedure:



                        Further
                        Teaching
                        Suggestions:
```

Other Features Include:

Example Pages give the teacher and students a sample of how to proceed with an activity.

Student Activity Pages could be reproduced or laminated for student use. Most of these Activity Pages invite student manipulation of materials directly on the page. Directions are aimed at the student and are generally brief.

Color Cube Pattern Pages provide design arrangements for the Color Cubes. A coding system describes the Color Cubes and their arrangement.

An **Appendix** provides solutions to problems and puzzles. Directions for making Game Cards are also included.

In a separate packet which accompanies the book are various **Loop Activity cards** which are used in many of the games and activities.

One-Loop Activity Cards are provided for both the Attribute Blocks and People Pieces. All single attribute subsets of each material are pictured.

Two-Loop Activity Cards are provided for both Attribute Blocks and People Pieces. Two overlapping loops picture the unions and intersections of various pairs of sets.

Three-Loop Activity Cards are provided for both Attribute Blocks and People Pieces. Three overlapping loops picture the unions and intersections of various triples of sets.

Puzzle Activity Cards picture one, two and three loop arrangements of Attribute Blocks or People Pieces. The challenge is to determine which pieces complete the sets or which sets are represented based on the information provided.

Label Cards for Attribute Blocks and People Pieces are included with the Loop Activity Cards. Once they are cut to size, they will be used in many of the activities.

ATTRIBUTE GAMES AND ACTIVITIES is intended to provide enjoyable learning experiences in a variety of modes. Hopefully, it will act as a beginning for the development of new concepts and activities in the exciting world of mathematics.

Attribute Games and Activities is designed to be used with Loop Activity Cards. The Loop Activity Card set consists of Label Cards, One-Loop, Two-Loop, Three-Loop and Puzzle Activity Cards. Most of the student activities can be done using the Label Cards which come with the A-Blocks and the People Pieces. However, nine activities require or suggest the use of the Loop Activity Cards. The Loop Activity Cards are available from:

Creative Publications, Inc.

P.O. Box 10328

Palo Alto, California 94303

ATTRIBUTE BLOCKS

ATTRIBUTE BLOCKS

Attribute Blocks consist of wooden pieces which have

Different Shapes:	Different Sizes:		Different Colors.
	large	small	
circle	◯	○	red R,r
square	◻	▢	yellow Y,y
triangle	△	△	green G,g
diamond	◇	◇	blue B,b

In the text, a code is used to indicate shape, color and size. Here are some of the pieces:

Large, red circle　　(R)

Small, red circle　　(r)

Large, blue diamond　〈B〉

Small, green triangle　△g

Initially, students develop a basic understanding of sets by sorting the blocks into subsets according to a particular attribute. A more advanced level of sorting evolves from comparing the blocks according to similarities and differences. The concepts of union and intersection emerge when the blocks are used with Venn diagrams.

Prior to beginning the activities, students should remove the blocks from their container and engage in a period of free play. The Label Cards, included in the set of Loop Activity Cards, should be cut into individual cards. Yarn loops, approximately 18″ in diameter, can be made by the teacher. Plastic loops are commercially available.

Unless otherwise specified, the activities are intended to be used with groups of three or four students. For most of the activities each group should be provided with one set of Attribute Blocks, one set of Label Cards and the specified number of loops.

12

SORTING ACTIVITY

Materials: Attribute Blocks
Label Cards without asterisks†

Procedure: After the students have had some free time to become familiar with the blocks, have them sort the blocks according to a systematic procedure. Then have them find Label Cards to describe their groups.

Further Teaching Suggestions: Students at all stages need some sorting activity to become familiar with the blocks. The younger the students the more time should be spent with the activity. With older students, less time can be spent in sorting before moving on to the next activity.

---

†Label Cards and Loop Activity Cards with asterisks indicate a "not" or negative set.

13

FINDING SUBSETS

Materials: Attribute Blocks
Label Cards without asterisks
One Loop

Procedure: Ask the students to put a specific group of blocks in a loop. For example, ''Put all the red blocks in a loop.'' The desk top would look like this:

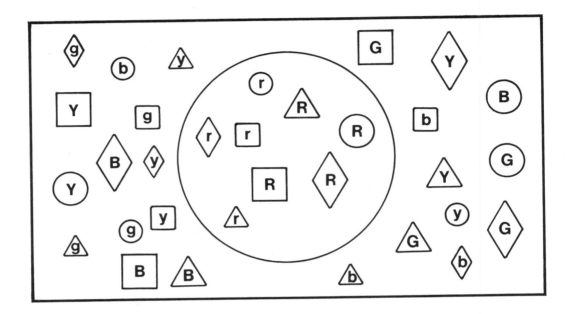

Ask the students to put other groups of blocks in a loop.

Further Teaching Suggestions: For older students this activity may become student-led by using Label Cards. A student shuffles the Label Cards and places them face down on the table. A card is turned up. The blocks are arranged in the loop according to the card. △ means

''Put all the triangles in a loop.'' Another card is turned up, and the activity is repeated. Students may record the results using drawings, or they may ask a friend to check the results.

14

"NOT" SETS

Materials: Attribute Blocks
Label Cards with and without asterisks
One Loop

Procedure: Show the students a Label Card with an asterisk on it. Explain that [not* red] means

"the pieces that are not red". Ask the students to place the blocks described by the

[not* red] Label Card in a loop. The desk top would look like this:

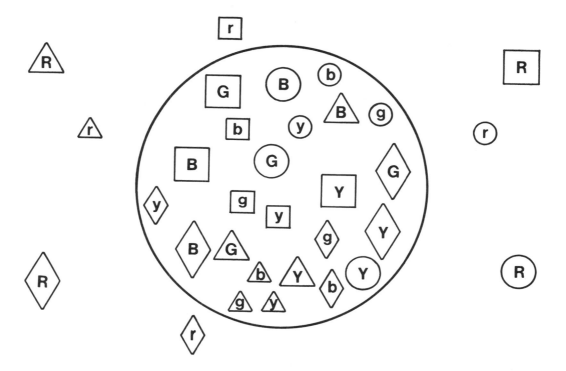

Point out that none of the pieces in the loop are red; all the red blocks are outside the loop. Show the students other "not" set Label Cards and ask them to place the appropriate blocks in the loop.

Further Teaching Suggestions: This activity may become student-led. A student shuffles the Label Cards and places them face down in the center of the table. A card is turned up. The blocks are placed in a loop according to the card. Another card is turned up and the activity is repeated. Students may record the results using drawings or they may ask a friend to check the results.

15

NAME THE SET

Materials: Attribute Blocks
One-Loop Activity Cards
Label Cards with and without asterisks

Procedure: Students try to match the correct Label Card with the set pictured inside the loop on the One-Loop Activity Card. For example, this Label Card ▢ is matched with this One-Loop Activity Card.

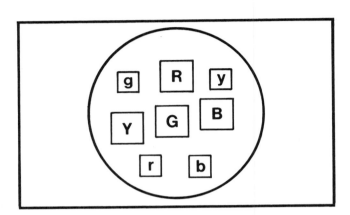

Further Teaching Suggestions: After the students have experienced this activity and are very familiar with the sub-sets you may want to ask them to note how many blocks there are in a specific set. For example:

"How many blocks are in the set of diamonds?"
"How many blocks are in the set of 'not-reds'?"

With younger students and certain older students continue to use the blocks to verify the work.

Have the students observe patterns such as:

Each positive, color Label Card gives a set with 8 members.
Each positive, shape Label Card gives a set with 8 members.
Each positive, size Label Card gives a set with 16 members.
Each negative ("not-set"), color Label Card gives a set with 24 members.
Each negative, shape Label Card gives a set with 24 members.
Each negative, size Label Card gives a set with 16 members.

Students may also note that Label Cards with asterisks may describe the blocks that fall outside the One-Loop Activity Cards without an asterisk.

CHALLENGE PROBLEMS

Have the students show with blocks or draw a picture of each of these sets. Describe each set with words.

1. A set with 16 members.
2. A set with 24 members.
3. A set with 4 members.
4. A set with 1 member.

16

MATCHING ACTIVITY

Materials: One-Loop Activity Cards without asterisks
Label Cards without asterisks

Procedure: Lay out the One-Loop Activity Cards on a table.

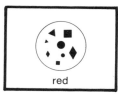
red

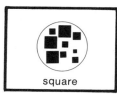
small

square

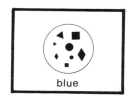
diamond

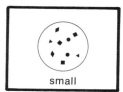
blue

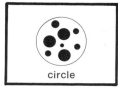
circle

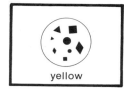
yellow

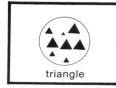
triangle

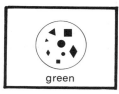
green

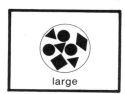
large

Give the students the Label Cards one at a time and ask them to place the Label Card on the One-Loop Activity Card which it matches.

Further Teaching Suggestions: Students should become familiar with all the one-attribute subsets of the blocks. After thorough exposure to these cards the activity could be extended by using the Label Cards and One-Loop Activity Cards with asterisks.

17

CONCENTRATION GAME†

Materials: One-Loop Activity Cards without asterisks
Label Cards without asterisks

Procedure: This is a game for two players or two teams. One player shuffles the One-Loop Activity Cards and arranges them face down, on the floor or on a large table, in two rows of five across. Next, the player shuffles the Label Cards and arranges them face down in two rows of five across, below the Activity Cards. The table should look like this:

Students alternate turning over an Activity Card and then a Label Card. If the Label Card names the blocks pictured in the loop, the player keeps the Activity Card and the Label Card and then takes a second turn. If the Label Card does not name the set of blocks pictured, the Activity Card and the Label Card are turned face down in their original positions.

The next player takes a turn. Play continues until all Activity Cards and Label Cards are removed from the table. The player who has the most "matches" wins.

Further Teaching Suggestions: As a challenge the Label Cards and One-Loop Activity Cards with asterisks may be used. This greatly increases the difficulty of the game.

---

†This game may be too difficult for younger students.

18

ATTRIBUTE CARD GAME

Materials: Attribute Blocks
Game Card Deck (A deck of 40 cards consisting of 4 cards for each value of color, shape and size. Directions for making the deck appear in the Appendix, page 144.)

Procedure: This game is best played with three or four players. The dealer chooses one block and places it in the center of the table. The dealer shuffles the cards and deals four cards face down to each player and one card face up, starting a discard pile. The remaining deck forms a draw pile.

The player to the left of the dealer draws first. A turn consists of selecting one card from either the draw or discard pile and then discarding one card. Play then moves clockwise. The winner of the hand is the first player to hold the three cards that exactly describe the block on the table. For example:

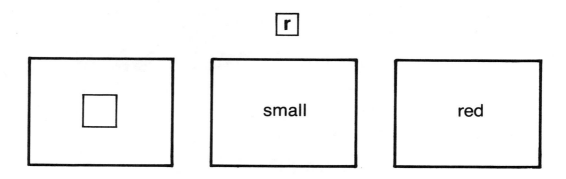

A game is over when each player has dealt once. The game winner is the player who had the greatest number of winning hands.

19

ARRANGING GAME

Materials: Attribute Blocks

Procedure: This game is played with a group of students and a leader. The leader directs players to arrange the blocks in some way on a table. After the blocks have been arranged, all the students close their eyes while the leader removes a block so the players do not see it.

When the leader gives a signal, the students open their eyes. The first person to guess the missing block becomes the leader for the next round.

Further Teaching Suggestions: Some arrangements make it easy to spot the missing block. Encourage the students to try different arrangements to determine the "best" arrangement.

As a variation of the game, students place the blocks on the table randomly rather than in a particular arrangement. Play the game as before. This requires the students to know all the blocks.

A follow-up Student Activity Page is found on the next page.

SOMEONE ELSE'S ARRANGEMENT

This is an arrangement of large blocks, what blocks are missing?

Y (square)			Y (rhombus)
		B (circle)	
	R (triangle)		
	G (triangle)		

How could all the blocks, large and small, be placed in this arrangement?

Attribute Games and Activities
©1976, Creative Publications, Inc.

TWENTY QUESTIONS GAME

Materials: Attribute Blocks

Procedure: This is a variation of the standard "Twenty Questions" game. Ask one student to think of a block. The student tells its name to the teacher or writes its name on a piece of paper without letting the other students see it. The other students, in turn, ask yes/no questions about the mystery block. After each question is answered, the students move to one side those blocks that do not fit the clues already disclosed.

A score keeper can count the number of questions asked. Students try to find the mystery block using the fewest questions possible.

Further Teaching Suggestions: Encourage students to ask more general questions at first, rather than questions about a specific block. For example, a general question might be:
"Is it blue?"
"Is it a member of the not-square set?"

Advanced students might ask questions such as
"Is it green or blue?"
"Is it large or red?"
These questions allow more blocks to be eliminated on a single turn.

A typical example of the game is shown on the next page.

AN EXAMPLE OF TWENTY QUESTIONS GAME

The blocks are placed in the center of the table.

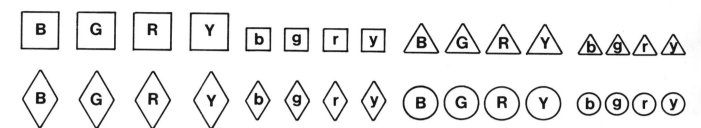

"Is it large?"   NO   All large blocks are removed.

"Does it have four sides?"   YES   Only those blocks with four sides remain.

"Is it green?"   NO

"Is it yellow?"   NO

"Is it square?"   YES

"Is it red?"   NO

THE MYSTERY PIECE IS [b], THE SMALL, BLUE SQUARE.

Attribute Games and Activities
©1976, Creative Publications, Inc.

WHO AM I? GAME

Materials: Attribute Blocks

Procedure: This game can be played by individuals or by teams. For younger students the teacher reads the clues. "Clue cards" can be prepared for older students. The players are shown a "clue card." The first player to discover the mystery piece is the winner. Four typical "clue cards" are shown:

(1)
Who am I?
I am large.
I am not yellow.
I have four sides.
I am not blue or green.
I am not a diamond.
Who am I?

(2)
Who am I?
I am not large.
I am green or red.
I am not four sided.
I have no corners.
I am not green.
Who am I?

(3)
Who am I?
I do not fit in a round hole.
I have four corners.
I am not red.
I am large.
I am green.
I am not square.
Who am I?

(4)
I am lost, help me find myself.
When you find me, hold me in your hand.
I am small.
I am not blue.
I am not square.
I am green.
I will roll off the table.

Further Teaching Suggestions: Write other "clue cards" for your students. Have older students write "clue cards." Have a contest for the most difficult or easiest. Ask students to discover the fewest number of clues necessary to find a piece.

Attribute Games and Activities
©1976, Creative Publications, Inc.

IN THE LOOP

Materials: Attribute Blocks
Label Cards without asterisks
One Loop

Procedure: This game is played by two players or two teams. Shuffle the Label Cards and place them face down in the center of the table. Place a loop on the table. One student picks a Label Card and looks at it without showing the other player and then places it face down on the loop.

The second player chooses a block and asks, "Does this piece go in the loop?" If the question is answered "yes", the player leaves the block in the loop. If the response is "no", the player places the block outside the loop. As soon as there are sufficient "clues", the second player tries to name the set described on the Label Card.

The goal of the game is to name the set with the fewest number of pieces attempted. After the set has been named correctly, count the number of pieces the player attempted to place; add five points for each incorrect attempt to name the set. This sum is the player's score. The winner is the player with the lowest score after 5 turns.

Further Teaching Suggestions: For a more difficult variation, use all the Label Cards.

This game could also be used as an introduction to the two-loop game "In the Loops" (page 50).

Use this game to help students see that as much information is gained by a "no" response as by a "yes" response.

25

SORTING ACCORDING TO DIFFERENCES AND SIMILARITIES

Materials: Attribute Blocks
Difference Activity Page (page 27)

Procedure: Ask students to compare blocks in terms of their differences and similarities. Hold up a block and ask the students to hold up a block which differs in one way. Repeat this with several blocks, then ask them to hold up a block which differs in two ways, then in three ways. At the same time, ask the students to hold up blocks that are similar in two, one or no ways.

After the students are familiar with comparing blocks according to their differences and similarities, give them the Difference Activity Page. Place a block in the top section and circle the number of differences that will determine the sorting. Ask the students to sort all the remaining blocks into those that belong in the bottom section and those that do not.

Further Teaching Suggestions: Two blocks may differ in one, two or three ways and at the same time be similar in two, one or no ways.

Other Student Activity Pages are provided on pages 28 and 29. These Student Activity Pages involve sorting according to specified differences.

26

DIFFERENCE ACTIVITY

Put one block here.

Circle one:

One Difference

Two Differences

Three Differences

Place in this box pieces that differ in the number of ways circled.

FOLLOW THE ARROWS

Put a block on START. Follow an arrow to another position and put a different block in the new position. The new block must be different only in the way named on the arrow.

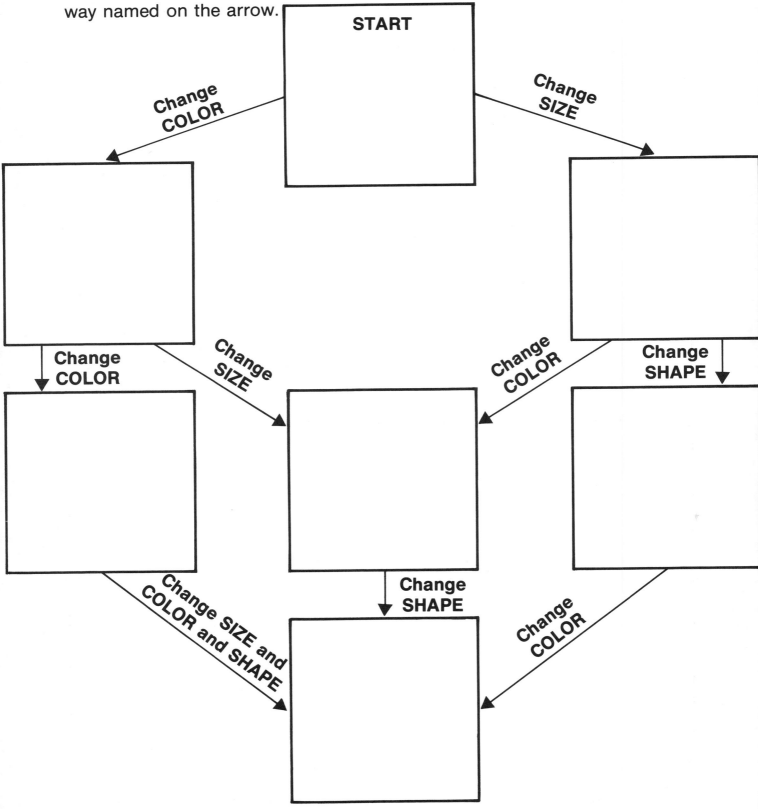

Attribute Games and Activities
©1976, Creative Publications, Inc.

A DIFFERENCE ACTIVITY

Put a block on START. Follow an arrow to another position and put another block in the new position. The new block must be different from the previous block in the number of ways indicated on the arrow.

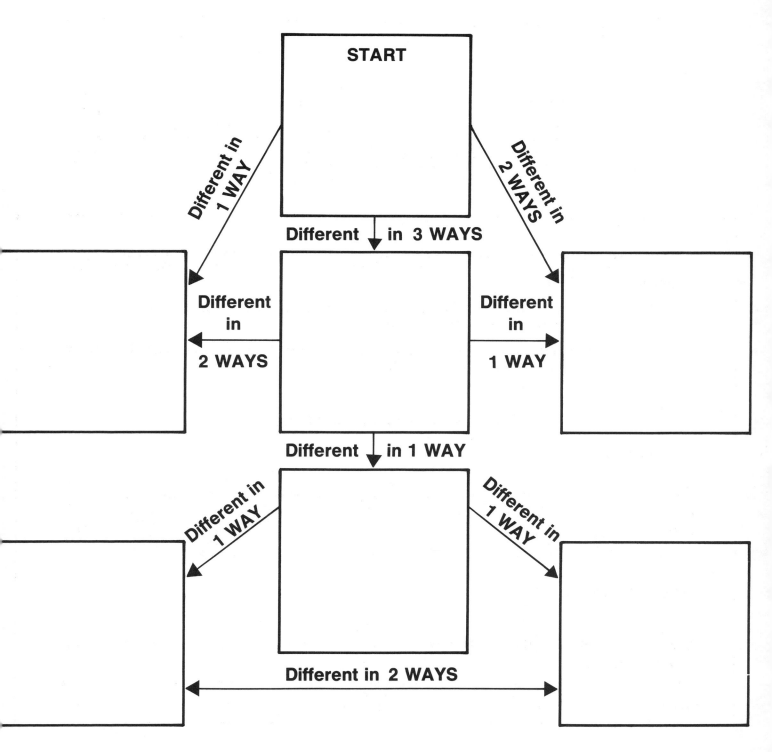

MAKING CHAINS AND TRAINS

Materials: Attribute Blocks

Procedure: Ask a student to choose a block. This block is the first block in a chain. Ask another student to choose a second block which is different from the first block in exactly one way. Place the second block next to the first block. Place a third block in the chain. It should differ from the second block in exactly one way.

Continue the chain until it has seven blocks. For example, ◇B is chosen for the first block.

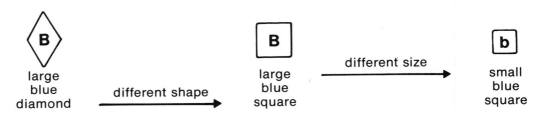

Further Teaching Suggestions: Have students continue the chain by asking the students to use all the blocks. Ask the students to form a circle out of the chain that uses all the blocks. Is it a one difference circle?

Have the students make two and three difference chains. Examples of two and three difference chains are given below.

Student Activity Pages follow using difference chains to make trains. Use these to extend this activity where appropriate.

EXAMPLES OF OTHER CHAINS

A TWO—DIFFERENCE CHAIN

A THREE—DIFFERENCE CHAIN

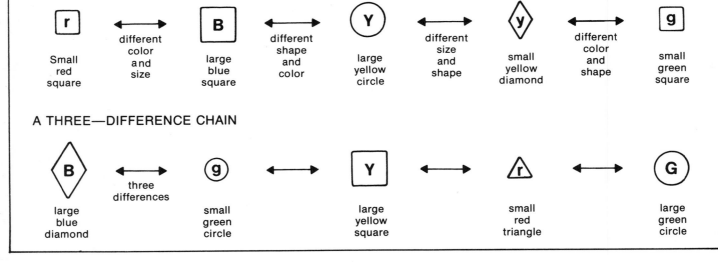

30

A DIFFERENCE TRAIN

Place one block in each car to make this a One-Difference Train. Each block must differ from the preceding block in exactly one way.

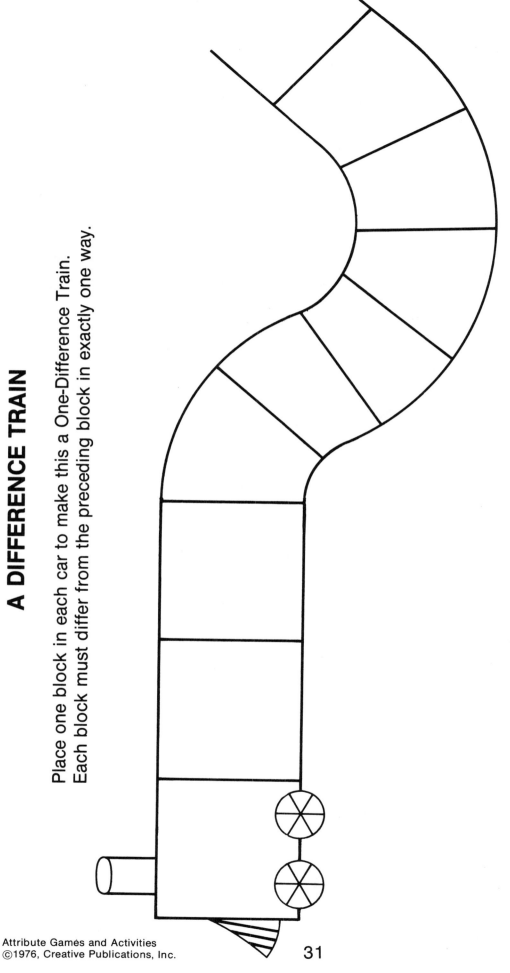

Make Another One—Difference Train.
Make A Two—Difference Train.
Make A Three—Difference Train.

A THREE-DIFFERENCE TRAIN

This is a Three-Difference Train. Each block is different from its neighbor in three ways. Fill in the missing cars.

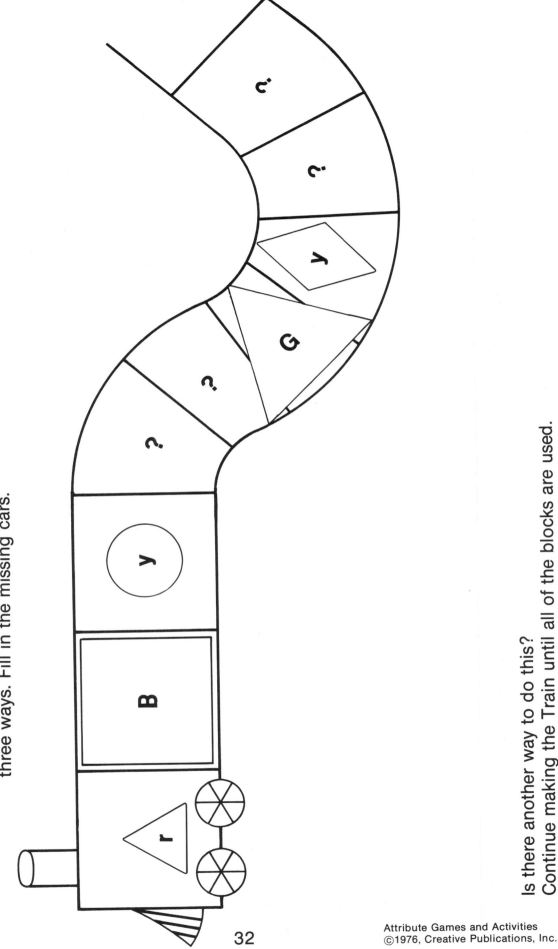

Is there another way to do this?
Continue making the Train until all of the blocks are used.

32

Attribute Games and Activities
©1976, Creative Publications, Inc.

MAKING OTHER ARRANGEMENTS

Materials: Attribute Blocks
Arranging Mats (pages 34, 35, 37, 39)

Procedure: Choose an Arranging Mat and have students place blocks on the mat so that each block is different from its neighbors, horizontally and vertically (but not diagonally) in exactly one way. Begin with the 2 x 2 mat and progress to more difficult ones. For example,

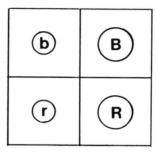

Further Teaching Suggestions: The Arranging Mats ask the students to extend their thinking by making arrangements with two differences and three differences. Student Activity Pages are also provided (pages 36, 38, and 40) which picture an arrangement with some blocks missing.

Younger students may need to color the blocks pictured on the Student Activity Pages or actually place blocks on the pages to find the missing pieces.

The rectangular and square arrangements become more difficult. Each block has either two, three or four neighbors instead of only two, as in the 2 x 2 arrangement.

As a challenge, ask students to make one-, two- or three-difference arrangements using only the large or small blocks.

33

2 x 2 ARRANGING MAT

Place the blocks on this mat so each block is different from its horizontal and vertical neighbors in exactly one way.

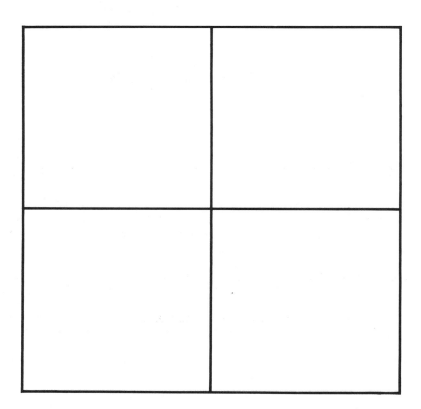

1. Repeat this with each block being different from its horizontal and vertical neighbors in exactly two ways.
2. Repeat this with each block being different from its horizontal and vertical neighbors in exactly three ways.

Attribute Games and Activities
©1976, Creative Publications, Inc.

The "H" MAT

Place the blocks on the mat so each block is different from its horizontal and vertical neighbors in exactly one way.

1. Repeat with each block being two different from its neighbors.
2. Do this again with each block being three different from its neighbors.

Attribute Games and Activities
©1976, Creative Publications, Inc.

WHAT IS MISSING IN THE TWO-DIFFERENCE "H"?

Using blocks, can you fill in the missing pieces?
Remember this is a two-difference H.

CHALLENGE: Joan used only these pieces.
Can you finish her arrangement?

Attribute Games and Activities
©1976, Creative Publications, Inc.

3 x 3 ARRANGING MAT

Place your blocks on this mat so each block differs from its horizontal and vertical neighbors in exactly one way.

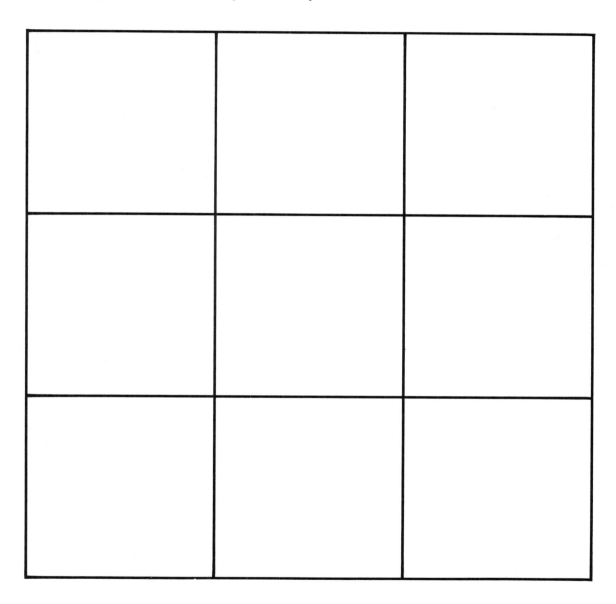

Make this a two-difference square.
Can you build a one-difference square using only large blocks?
If you can, is there more than one way to do it?

WHAT IS MISSING IN THE SQUARE?

This is a three-difference square. Use all of your blocks and find the missing pieces.

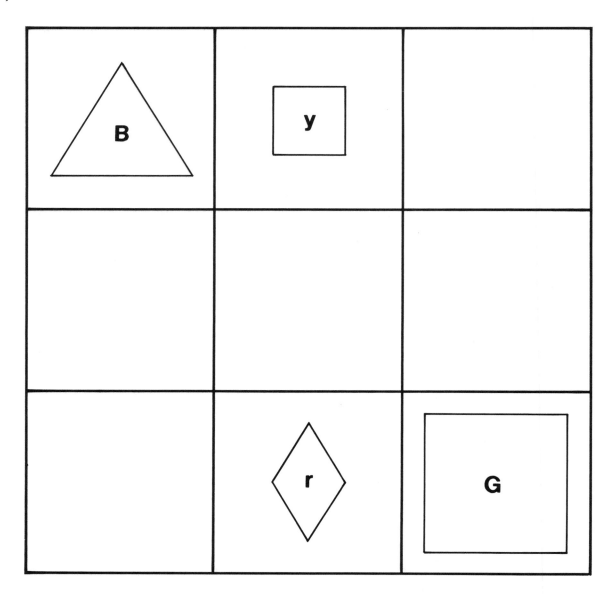

Is there any other solution? If so, how many different solutions can you find?

Attribute Games and Activities
©1976, Creative Publications, Inc.

4 x 4 ARRANGING MAT

Place your blocks on this mat so each block differs from its horizontal and vertical neighbors in exactly one way.

Make this a two-difference square. Make this a two-difference square using only large blocks. Can you do this in more than one way?

WHAT IS MISSING IN THE SQUARE?

This is a two-difference square. Use all your blocks and find the missing pieces.

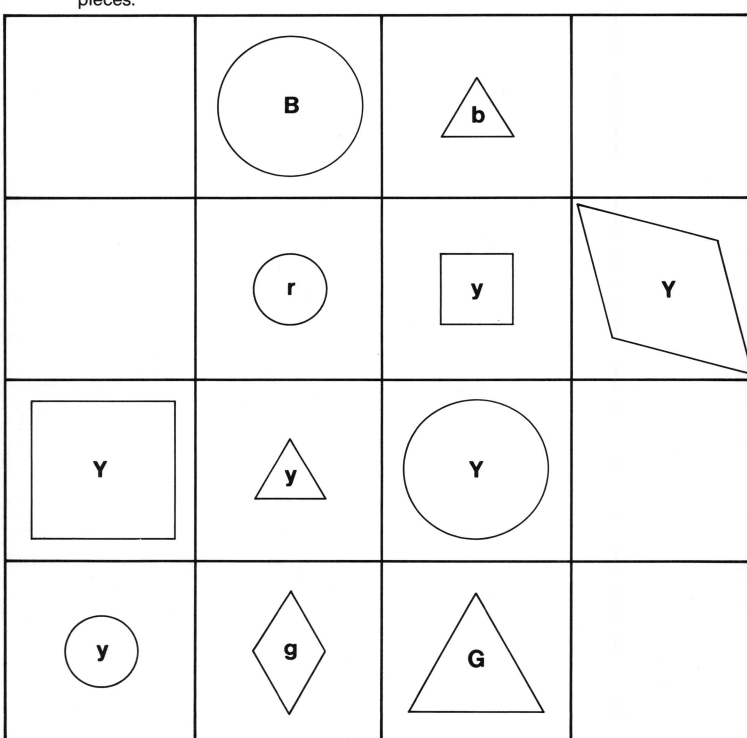

Do this again using only your large blocks. Can you complete the two-difference square using only large blocks? If so, is there more than one way to do it?

40

WATCH IT! GAME

Materials: Attribute Blocks
WATCH IT! Game Mat (next page)
Paper Bag

Procedure: This game is played with two players. The Attribute Blocks are placed in a paper bag and "shuffled". One player takes a block from the bag and places it on any square of the game mat. The other player takes one block from the bag and places it on another square of the game mat.

THE ONLY RULE is that no two blocks with the same color or shape may be placed in the same row, column or diagonal.

If a player cannot place a block on the game mat, the block is given to the opposing player and added to his "scoring stack". If a player places a block so it completes "four in a line", the player receives a block from the opponent's "scoring stack". If the opponent has no blocks, a block is taken from the bag. Play continues until all the blocks in the bag are used. The winner is the player who has the most blocks in his "scoring stack".

Further Teaching Suggestions: Ask students to discover a way of placing all the large pieces on the WATCH IT! Game mat so that no two blocks with the same color or shape are in the same row, column or diagonal.

41

WATCH IT! GAME MAT

Attribute Games and Activities
©1976, Creative Publications, Inc.

DIFFERENCE GAME

Materials: Attribute Blocks
Difference Game Mat (next page)

Procedure: This is a game for two players or two teams. The blocks are randomly divided between the two players, so each has 16 blocks. A turn consists of placing a block on the game mat.

THE ONLY RULE is that a block must differ from its horizontal and vertical neighbors in exactly two ways. The first player who cannot place a block loses.

Further Teaching Suggestions: The "only rule" can be varied to one or three differences to make the game simpler or more difficult.

Use any of the Arranging Mats. Play with only small or large blocks to vary the game.

DIFFERENCE GAME MAT

TWO-LOOP PROBLEMS†

Materials: Attribute Blocks
Label Cards without asterisks
Two Loops

Procedure: Place the two loops on a table as shown below. Select two Label Cards which describe sets with no common pieces. For example: ☐ and △ . The table top will look like this:

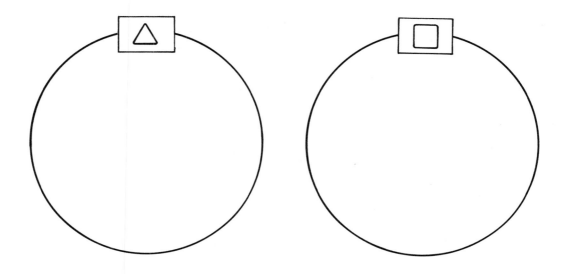

Have the students place the pieces on the table where they belong (either in one of the loops if squares or triangles or outside the loops). After all of the pieces have been placed have the children carefully check to see that all pieces have been correctly placed.

Repeat this activity using pairs of cards such as blue/green, circle/diamond, large/small, triangle/circle, red/yellow, etc. Stress checking the loops after all pieces have been placed to see if all pieces are correctly located.

---

†This activity is designed to lead into the discovery of intersection.

MORE TWO-LOOP PROBLEMS

Materials: Attribute Blocks
Label Cards without asterisks

Procedure: Place two loops on the table so they do not overlap. Now place the Label Cards for blue and triangle on the loops and have the students place the blocks. The students need to be guided to discover that the blue triangles must be in both loops at the same time. Let the students discover this can be accomplished by overlapping the loops. Do not tell the students to do this. The arrangement may look like this.

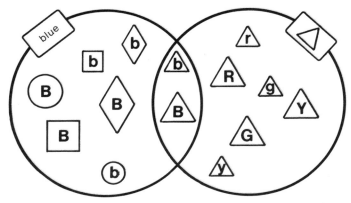

After the students have made the discovery of overlapping the loops, extend this activity by considering other pairs of sets such as: red/square, circle/small, yellow/diamond, large/triangle, red/green, large/not small.

Further Teaching Suggestions:	Let students discover the concept of intersection by leading a discussion. A possible discussion might be:

Teacher: Let's check each loop and see if all the pieces are in the right loops. Are all the blue pieces in the loop with the blue Label Card?

Child: Yes.

Teacher: Good. Now let's look at the other loop. Are all the triangles in it?

Child: No.

Teacher: Which ones are missing?

Child: The blue ones.

One of the children will probably move the blue triangles to the loop labeled triangles. When this happens ask: Is this loop now complete?

Child: Yes.

Teacher: Let's check the other loop again. Are all the blue pieces in it?

Child: No, the blue triangles are missing.

Again, one of the children will probably move the blue triangles to the blue loop.

Teacher: We seem to have a problem with the blue triangles. They belong in both loops at the same time. What can we do?

This approach most often will end with one of the students suggesting overlapping the loops and placing the blue triangles in the region where the loops overlap.

46

TWO-LOOP ACTIVITY

Materials: Attribute Blocks
Label Cards without asterisks
Two Loops

Procedure: Place two overlapping loops on the table. Shuffle the Label Cards and place a Label Card on each of the loops. A student places the Attribute Blocks in the loops in their correct positions. Repeat this activity with other Label Cards in the loops.

Further Teaching Suggestions: Use all the Label Cards to increase the difficulty of this activity.

47

UNIONS AND INTERSECTIONS

Materials: Attribute Blocks
Label Cards without asterisks
Two Loops
Two-Loop Activity Cards without asterisks

Procedure: Pose a two-loop problem for the students to solve by turning over two Label Cards. Students should place all the blocks appropriately. For example,

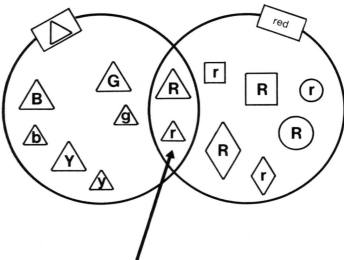

Define the sections of the loops. The blocks that are in both loops are placed here because they are both red *and* triangle. This is called the **INTERSECTION†** of the two sets.

The blocks that are in either one loop or the other, or both are called the **UNION** of the two sets. The blocks in the union are in either the red set or the triangle set, or both. The blocks which are not in the intersection may be described as "triangle but not red," or "red but not triangle."

Further Teaching Suggestions: Using blocks and two overlapping loops, one student places the blocks in the loops and challenges another student to name the sets, their union and intersection.

Using Two-Loop Activity Cards, one student shows his partner a card. His partner must name the sets pictured, their union and intersection.

---

†The set terminology, union and intersection, is used only in four or five activities. The extent to which you use the terms depends on the age of your students, the math program you are using and your own discretion.

INTERSECTION GAME

Materials: Attribute Blocks†
One-Loop Activity Cards without asterisks

Procedure: This game is for two players or two teams. One player shuffles the deck of One-Loop Activity Cards and places them face down in the center of the table and turns over two Activity Cards so all the players can see them. Both players attempt to place the blocks that are in the intersection on the table (an alternative is to record this information on paper).

The first player to show the blocks in the intersection names the two sets and the intersection. If the response is correct the player scores one point. If incorrect, the other player has a chance to respond; if correct, the second player scores the point. The first person to score 5 points wins.

Further Teaching Suggestions: The teacher can direct this game and play with the entire class. For a more difficult version, use all the One-Loop Activity Cards.

---

†With young students each player or team should have a set of blocks to show the answer. Older students can use paper and pencil to indicate their response.

49

IN THE LOOPS

Materials: Attribute Blocks
Label Cards without asterisks
Two Loops

Procedure: This game is played by two players or two teams. Shuffle the Label Cards and place them face down in the center of the table. Place the two loops so they overlap as shown below. One student picks two Label Cards and looks at them without showing the other player, then places them face down, one on each loop. The second player chooses a block and tries to locate the section of the loops where it belongs.

For example, if these cards were drawn by the first player: △ , red the second player may choose **b** and ask, "Does this piece go here?"

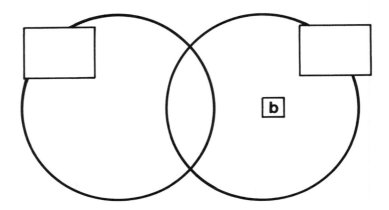

If the question is answered "yes", the player can leave the block in that region. A "no" response may mean the player should try another region or that the piece does not belong in either loop. A piece which belongs in the intersection should receive a "yes" response only when placed in the intersection.

As soon as there are sufficient "clues," the second player tries to name the two sets.

The goal of the game is to name the sets with the fewest number of pieces attempted.

When both sets have been named, count the number of pieces the player attempted to place; add five points for each incorrect attempt to name a set. This sum is the player's score. The winner is the player, or team, with the *lowest* score after an agreed upon number of turns.

Further Teaching Suggestions: For a more difficult variation, use all the Label Cards. For many students, a review of the one-loop game "In the Loop" (page 25) may be necessary.

It is important that students understand that they gain as much information from a "no" response as from a "yes" response.

WHAT'S MISSING? GAME

Materials: Attribute Blocks
Label Cards without asterisks
Puzzle Activity Cards without asterisks
Marker for each player

Procedure: This is a game for four or five players. A non-playing leader shuffles the Puzzle Activity Cards and places them face down in the center of the table and then turns over one Puzzle Activity Card for all the players to see. When a player knows the blocks or Label Cards that replace the question mark, he hands his marker to the leader. The next player who knows the missing blocks or Label Cards gives his marker to the leader and so on until the leader has all the markers.

The leader asks the player who was first to name all the missing blocks or Label Cards. If the first player makes an error the second player names the missing blocks. If that answer is not completely correct, the next player tries and so on. The player who correctly names all the missing blocks scores 1 point. The first player to score 5 points wins.

Further Teaching Suggestions: Use all Label Cards and Puzzle Activity Cards to challenge older students.

MATCH GAME

Materials: Two-Loop Activity Cards
Deck of Game Cards (see Appendix)

Procedure: This game is for two to four players.

The dealer shuffles the deck of Two-Loop Activity Cards and deals two cards face down to each player. Players look at their own Activity Cards and replace them on the table face down. The dealer shuffles the Game Cards, deals three cards to each player and places the rest of the deck face down in the center of the table.

The goal of the game is to match a Two-Loop Activity Card with its appropriate Game Cards. For example,

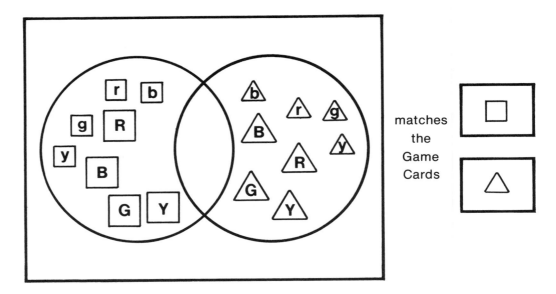

On a turn, a player takes one card from the deck of Game Cards in the center of the table and discards one card face up in the center of the table. The next player may either take a card from the deck or the discard pile.

When a player has a match, the Activity Card is turned over and the matching Game Cards are placed on the correct loops. The player does not discard a card. The Winner is the first player who matches both Activity Cards with Game Cards.

Further Teaching Suggestions: As a further challenge deal 3 Two-Loop Activity Cards and five Game Cards to each player; game proceeds as above.

52

THREE-LOOP PROBLEMS

Materials: Attribute Blocks
Label Cards without asterisks
Three Loops

Procedure: Pose a two-loop problem. By now students should be familiar with the two-loop arrangement and should be able to easily place the blocks appropriately. For example, the sets red and square are arranged:

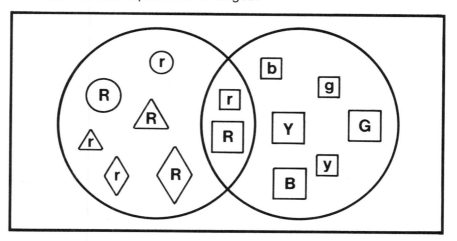

Now ask the students to place another loop on this arrangement and place all the large blocks in this third loop. Using a method similar to that described on page 46 for two-loop problems, guide the discovery of the three-loop arrangement shown below.

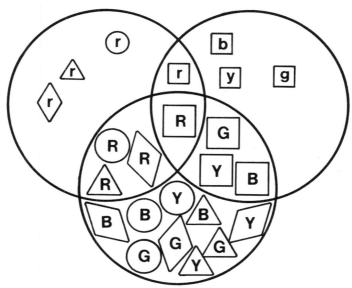

Pose other three-loop problems for the students to solve.

Further Teaching Suggestions: Describe the various regions of the three-loop arrangement. For example, find the region or regions for (1) red and square, (2) red and square and large, (3) large and red but not square, (4) square or large.

In doing three-loop problems, rigid loops (coat hangers, or commercial plastic ones) are preferable, since the arrangement of regions remains unclear.

53

THREE-LOOP GAMES

Materials: Attribute Blocks
Label Cards without asterisks
Game Cards (see Appendix)
Three-Loop Activity Cards

Procedure: Make a three-loop arrangement. Choose three Label Cards and place each card on a loop. Now place all the blocks appropriately.

Many of the games and activities described for Two-Loop Activities may be adapted to Three-Loop Activities by using Three-Loop Activity Cards or by choosing three Label Cards or Game Cards instead of two.

Some suggested activities include:

UNIONS AND INTERSECTIONS	page 48
INTERSECTION GAME	page 49
IN THE LOOPS	page 50
WHAT'S MISSING? GAME	page 51
MATCH GAME	page 52

Further Teaching Suggestions: As variations to all these activities, the full deck of Label Cards may be used. Three-Loop problems involving not-sets become quite difficult.

BE A DETECTIVE

After Jane finished working on this three-loop problem her loops looked like this.

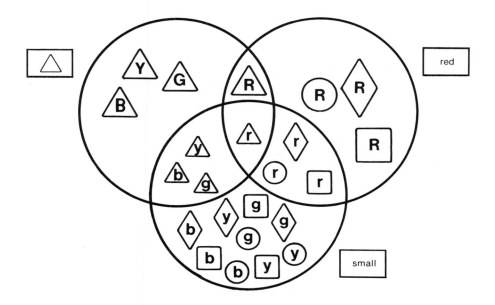

Answer the questions about Jane's work on page 56.

DETECTIVE QUESTIONS

Use Jane's Three-Loop Activity Page to answer these questions.
Use drawings to record your answers.

1. Where are the blocks that are both red and small? Name them.

2. Where are the blocks that are red and small and triangle? Name them.

3. How many blocks are small? _____
4. How many blocks are in the red, but not △ nor small? _____
5. How many blocks are red or triangle or small? _____
6. How many blocks are triangle or small? _____
7. How many blocks are in the triangle loop? _____
8. What blocks are small and triangle but not red?

9. What blocks are not triangle or red?

10. What blocks are small and red but not triangle?

Attribute Games and Activities
©1976, Creative Publications, Inc.

PEOPLE PIECES

PEOPLE PIECES

A set of People Pieces consists of sixteen plastic tiles on which people are drawn. The people differ with respect to:

sex: male or female
age: adult or child
girth: fat or thin
color of clothing: red or blue

female
child
fat
red

male
adult
thin
blue

Since the tiles picture people, younger students are often intrigued by People Pieces. They assign personalities to the figures and tell interesting stories about them.

People Pieces can be used with many of the same activities developed with Attribute Blocks. Since there are only two values for each attribute, not-sets are simpler than with Attribute Blocks. However, this very "two-ness" poses some interesting problems for older students.

Prior to beginning the activities, students should remove the People Pieces from their container and engage in a period of free play. The Label Cards should be cut into individual cards. Yarn loops, approximately 18" in diameter should also be made by the teacher for use in some of the games. Plastic loops are commercially available.

Unless otherwise specified, the activities are intended to be used with groups of three or four students. Each group should be provided with one set of People Pieces, one set of Label Cards, and the appropriate number of loops.

FINDING SUBSETS

Materials: People Pieces
Label Cards
One Loop

Procedure: Ask the students to put a specific set of People Pieces in a loop. For example:

"Put all the thin people in a loop."

"Put all the females in a loop."

"Put all the people that are not children in a loop."

Then ask them to find the Label Card which names the set. With young students the goal is to have them name each of the subsets and know that no tiles are missing.

Further Teaching Suggestions: This same activity can be experienced at a more abstract level. Have the students shuffle the Label Cards and place them face down. As a card is turned over, students place the appropriate tiles in a loop. | male | means "Put all the males in a loop."

Students may record the results with drawings or by having a friend check the tiles in the loop.

As a follow-up activity, students may observe patterns such as:
Positive, color sets (red, blue) have 8 tiles.
Sex sets (male, female) have 8 tiles.
Girth sets (fat, thin) have 8 tiles.
Age sets (adult, child) have 8 tiles.

As a challenge ask:
"How many tiles in the set of pieces which are both male and fat people?"
"How many tiles in the set of pieces which are either blue or child?"
"Find a set with 8 tiles, 4 tiles, 12 tiles, 2 tiles, 14 tiles, 1 tile."

59

ARRANGING THE TILES GAME

Materials: People Pieces

Procedure: This game is played with a group of students and a leader. Arrange the tiles randomly face up so all can see. Students observe the tiles for a moment and then close their eyes while the leader removes a tile. The leader hides the chosen tile so the others do not see it.

When the leader gives a signal, the students open their eyes and try to guess the missing tile. After a few initial guesses, the students are allowed to rearrange the tiles in some orderly fashion.

The first person to guess the missing tile correctly becomes the leader for the next round. Play the game as before. At the beginning of each subsequent round, arrange the tiles in some ordered way.

Further Teaching Suggestions: Some arrangements make it easy to spot the missing tiles. Encourage the students to try different arrangements to determine the kind of pattern that is most useful.

As a variation, place the tiles in a random arrangement throughout the game. This variation requires that the students know all the tiles in the set.

A Student Activity Page follows which may assist students in finding a useful arrangement.

SOMEONE ELSE'S ARRANGEMENT

Tom arranged his blocks this way.
Can you see a pattern to the rows and columns?

Find the missing tiles.

NAME THE SET

Materials: One-Loop Activity Cards for People Pieces
Label Cards

Procedure: Ask the students to match the Label Cards with the One-Loop Activity Cards. For example,

fat

Further Teaching Suggestions: Not-sets are not pictured separately, since each One-Loop Activity Card can be described in two ways.

The People Pieces pictured inside the loop may be described as: (1) people wearing blue or (2) people not wearing red. Students should be encouraged to describe each One-Loop Activity Card in two ways—by its positive and negative name.

CONCENTRATION GAME

Materials: One-Loop Activity Cards for People Pieces
Label Cards

Procedure: One player shuffles the One-Loop Activity Cards and arranges them on a large table face down in two rows of four across. Another player shuffles the Label Cards and arranges them face down in two rows of four across, below the Activity Cards. The table should look like this:

Students alternate, turning over an Activity Card and then a Label Card. If the Label Card names the People Pieces pictured in the loop, the player keeps the Activity Card and the Label Card and takes a second turn. If the Label Card does not name the set of People Pieces pictured, the Activity Card and Label Card are turned face down in their original positions. The next player takes a turn. Continue playing until all Activity Cards and Label Cards are removed from the table. The player who has the most cards wins.

FINDING DIFFERENCES AND SIMILARITIES

Materials: People Pieces

Procedure: Ask the students to compare pairs of tiles. Students should identify and count the differences and similarities between them. They should notice that the sum of the differences and similarities between two pieces always equals four.
For example:

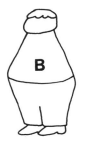
fat
male
adult
wearing
blue

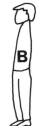
thin
male
adult
wearing
blue

ONE—
DIFFERENCE
PAIR
different girth
same sex
same age
same color clothing

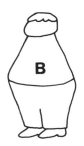
fat
male
adult
wearing
blue

thin
female
adult
wearing
blue

TWO—
DIFFERENCE
PAIR
different girth
different sex
same age
same color clothing

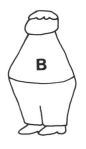
fat
male
adult
wearing
blue

thin
female
child
wearing
blue

THREE—
DIFFERENCE
PAIR
different girth
different sex
different age
same color clothing

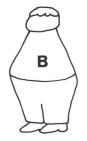
fat
male
adult
wearing
blue

thin
female
child
wearing
red

FOUR—
DIFFERENCE
PAIR
different girth
different sex
different age
different color clothing

Ask the students to find other pairs and name their differences and similarities.

64

SPECIAL ARRANGEMENTS

Materials: People Pieces
Special Arrangements, Activity Page (page 66)

Procedure: Three People Pieces are arranged in a partial square array as shown below.

Compare the tiles in the top row:

fat	thin	different girth
adult	adult	same age
female	female	same sex
red	blue	different color

There are **TWO DIFFERENCES:** girth and color. Therefore, a tile placed in the vacant position must be different from the tile to its left in two ways—girth and color.

thin			
adult			
male			
blue			

Missing tile.

fat	different girth
adult	same age
male	same sex
red	different color

65

SPECIAL ARRANGEMENTS ACTIVITY

Attribute Games and Activities
©1976, Creative Publications, Inc.

ALIKE/DIFFERENCE SORTING

Materials: People Pieces
Alike/Difference Sorting Mat

Procedure: Select a tile and put it in the first row of the sorting mat. In the second row, place all the tiles that differ from the original tile in exactly one way. Record the number of tiles in the row.

In the third row, place all the tiles that differ from the original tile in exactly two ways. Note the number of tiles. In the fourth row, place all the tiles that differ in exactly three ways from the original tile. Record the number. In the fifth row place all the tiles that differ in exactly four ways from the original tile. Record the number. For example,

AN EXAMPLE
ALIKE/DIFFERENCE SORTING MAT

Choose different original tiles and repeat activity.

Further Teaching Suggestions: After repeating this activity several times, ask students if there is a pattern emerging. Encourage students to describe aloud the differences as the tiles are placed in each row.

ALIKE/DIFFERENCE SORTING MAT

Number o
tiles in rov

Put a piece here	
Pieces that are different in one way	
Pieces that are different in two ways	
Pieces that are different in three ways	
Pieces that are different in four ways	

Attribute Games and Activities
©1976, Creative Publications, Inc.

TWO-LOOP PROBLEMS

Materials: People Pieces
Label Cards
Two Loops

Procedure: Place the two loops on the table or floor. The teacher chooses two label cards, one for each value of the same attribute, e.g. red, blue—different values for the color attribute. Place one card on each loop. Have the students place the tiles in the loops according to the cards.

Encourage students to discuss what is alike or different between each pair of sets. (There are only four such pairs of sets.)

Further Teaching Suggestions: This activity is intended to lead to the next activity which considers the intersection of two sets. (See the TWO-LOOP PROBLEMS for Attribute Blocks, page 45, for additional ideas.)

69

MORE TWO-LOOP PROBLEMS

Materials: People Pieces
Label Cards
Two Loops

Procedure: Ask the students to place all the females in one loop and then all the red pieces in a second loop. Lead the students to discover the necessity for overlapping the loops to accommodate those tiles which are both red and female.† Continue this activity by describing other pairs of sets and having the students place the tiles appropriately.

Further Teaching Suggestions: Eventually, this can be a student-led activity. Have students select two Label Cards to name the loops.

---

†If students have not worked two-loop intersection problems before see the development for Attribute Blocks on page 46. Use a similar development for People Pieces.

TWO-LOOP ACTIVITY

Materials: People Pieces
Label Cards
Two Loops

Procedure: This is an activity for one or two students, or two groups of students. Shuffle the deck of Label Cards and place it face down in the center of the table. Place two overlapping loops on the table. A student turns over two Label Cards and puts one card face up on each loop. The second student must place all of the pieces in their correct positions.

Further Teaching Suggestions: This can be a solitaire activity in which one person turns over the cards and places the pieces.

71

UNIONS AND INTERSECTIONS

Materials: People Pieces
Label Cards
Two Loops

Procedure: Give the students a two-loop problem to solve. Students should place all the tiles appropriately. For example,

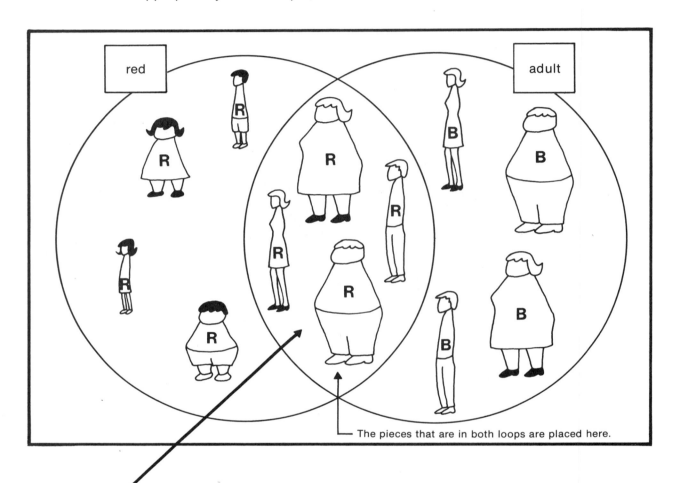

— The pieces that are in both loops are placed here.

This is called the **INTERSECTION** of the two sets. These pieces are in both the red set and the adult set. The pieces that are in either one loop or the other or both are called the **UNION** of the two sets; that is, the pieces in the union are in either the red set or the adult set or both. Some pieces are in only one loop or the other; these pieces are "red and not adult", or "adult and not red."

Have one student place the pieces in the loops according to two Label Cards chosen. The other students name the sets, their union and their intersection.

Further Teaching Suggestions: The terms union and intersection are used in only four or five activities. Your use of these terms depends on the age of your students, the math series you use and your discretion. For an independent student activity involving intersections see the Intersection Game for Attribute Blocks on page 49. Another game involving intersections is In the Loops on page 50.

72

WHAT'S MISSING? GAME

Materials:
People Pieces
Puzzle Activity Cards for People Pieces
A marker for each player

Procedure:
This is a game for four or five players. A leader shuffles the Puzzle Activity Cards and places them in a pile face down in the center of the table. The leader then turns over one Puzzle Activity Card for all the players to see.

When a player knows the piece, pieces or Label Card that replaces the question mark, he hands his marker to the leader. The next player who knows the missing pieces gives his marker to the leader and so on until the leader has all the markers.

The leader asks the player who was first to name the missing tiles or Label Cards. If that answer is not completely correct the next player tries and so on. The player who correctly names all the missing tiles or Label Cards scores one point. The first player to score 5 points wins.

MISSING PERSONS

Materials: People Pieces
"Clue" Cards (see below)

Procedure: Prepare "Clue" cards (samples shown below) and have the students play a game. The student who discovers the missing piece scores one point. After going through all the cards the student with the most points wins. Have students write their own "Clue" cards.

Sample "Clue" cards:

A People Piece has been reported missing. Help find the missing person.
1. The person is not adult.
   The person is thin.
   The person is female.
   The person was last seen in red clothes.

2. The person is adult.
   The person is not thin.
   The person is wearing blue.
   The person is not male.

3. The missing person is a child who was last seen riding his bike. His mother reports he was wearing a blue shirt and blue pants. He is also very thin.

74

THREE-LOOP PROBLEMS

Materials: People Pieces
Label Cards
Three Loops

Procedure: By now students should be familiar with an arrangement of loops for two sets. Ask the students to put two sets in the appropriate regions of the loops. For example, ''Put all the females in one loop and all the adults in another loop.''

Now ask students to add another loop for another set.
''Put all the fat people in a loop.'' The third loop must overlap each of the three original regions.

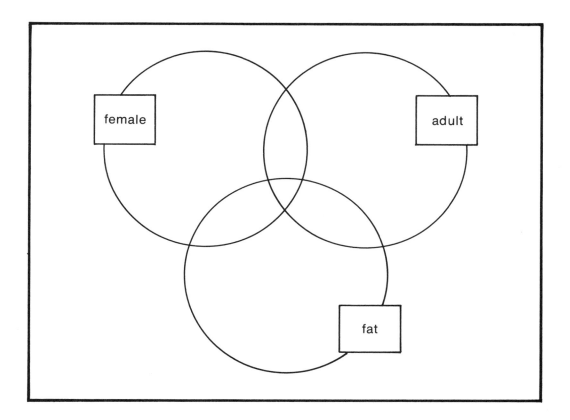

Students are asked to solve other three-loop problems.

Further Teaching Suggestions: This activity may become student-led by having students turn over three Label Cards to name the three sets.
Ask the students to describe all the regions of the three-loop arrangement. For example,
''In what region are the pieces that are: fat and adult; not female; female and fat, but not adult; fat and adult and female; adult, but not fat nor female?''

75

THREE-LOOP CHALLENGE GAME

Materials: People Pieces
Label Cards
Three Loops

Procedure: This is a game for two players. Place the People Pieces face down on the playing surface, "shuffle" them well and deal 8 pieces to each player.

One player chooses 3 Label Cards, looks at them without letting the other player see them and places one card face down on each loop. He then places his People Pieces in the proper regions of the three-loop arrangement. The second player observes the placement of pieces, but not the Label Cards, and then places his People Pieces where he thinks they belong.

The three Label Cards are turned over. The two players decide whether the second player placed his pieces correctly. If so, the second player scores 1 point. Take all the pieces out of the loops, "shuffle" them and deal 8 pieces to each player. The second player now chooses three Label Cards and the games continues. The first player to score 5 points wins.

Further Teaching Suggestions: Many of the two- and three-loop activities and games developed for Attribute Blocks can be adapted for use with People Pieces. One of these activities is to have students match Label Cards with the Three-Loop Activity Cards for People Pieces.

COLOR CUBES

COLOR CUBES

A set of Color Cubes consists of wooden cubes of six different colors. The colors and the code used to describe them are:

$$Y = \text{yellow}$$
$$G = \text{green}$$
$$Bl = \text{blue}$$
$$Bk = \text{black}$$
$$W = \text{white}$$
$$R = \text{red}$$

Some of the concepts developed through Attribute Blocks and People Pieces, especially non-intersecting sets and subsets, are well illustrated with Color Cubes since there is only one attribute, namely color. The Color Cubes are also useful in developing the concepts of permutations, combinations and tranformations.

Many of the activities involve the use of Color Cube Pattern Pages which are provided. The Pattern Pages should be colored before use so the sheets more closely duplicate actual arrangements of cubes. After the letter code is introduced, the students can color each Pattern Page with crayon or felt tip pen.

The Color Cube Pattern Pages may be used at four levels:

Concrete	By placing Color Cubes directly on the pages. Students respond by showing their arrangement of cubes.
Semi-concrete	By using colored pages and building the pattern next to it. The work is done with cubes, and the students respond by recording their results in color on graph paper.
Semi-abstract	By using colored pages and thinking through the problems with cubes. The work may be done by "reading" the pages rather than manipulating the cubes. The students respond by recording their results in color on graph paper.
Abstract	By using the black and white coded Pattern Pages. The students think through the problems and respond by recording their results with the letter code.

Before introducing the formal activities to the students, the teacher should plan for one or more periods of free play with the Color Cubes. Since Color Cube Graph Paper (page 80 or 81) is used repeatedly to do the problems and to record results, an adequate supply should be available at the start of this unit.

Unless otherwise indicated, each activity is intended for a group of four to five students. Each group should have a set of Color Cubes and several pieces of graph paper. Duplicate sets of the Pattern Pages may be provided for each student or pair of students. A large loop, approximately 18″ in diameter, and a smaller loop approximately 10″ in diameter should be made for use in some of the activities.

MAKING AND COPYING DESIGNS

Materials: Color Cubes
Color Cube Graph Paper
Color Cube Pattern Pages, 1–8 (pages 82–89)

Procedure: Ask the students to make a design using the cubes. After making the designs, ask students to record their design by coloring the graph paper.

Further Teaching Suggestions: Give the students Color Cube Pattern Pages and ask them to use the cubes to make the design on the table. Students may also use the patterns they have created on graph paper in the previous activity.

To extend this activity, students may be asked to repeat a particular pattern. For example, "Repeat this design twice."

To vary this activity, students might be asked to cover the tabletop by repeating a pattern.

Larger sheets of graph paper (12 x 12 or 20 x 20) can be made by taping or pasting pieces of the 6 x 6 or 10 x 10 paper together.

79

COLOR CUBE GRAPH PAPER

6 x 6

COLOR CUBE GRAPH PAPER

10 x 10

PATTERN PAGE 1

B_L	G
G	B_L

R	G
Y	B_L

B_K	W
W	W

Y	G
Y	G

82

Attribute Games and Activities
©1976, Creative Publications, Inc.

PATTERN PAGE 2

B_L	B_L	Y
Y	Y	B_L

Y	G	B_L
R	B_K	W

R	G	R
G	R	G
R	G	R

PATTERN PAGE 3

R	B_K	G	Y
B_K	R	B_K	G
B_K	G	B_K	R
G	Y	R	B_K

R	B_L	B_L	R
G	Y	Y	G
G	Y	Y	G
R	B_L	B_L	R

Attribute Games and Activities
©1976, Creative Publications, Inc.

PATTERN PAGE 4

B_K	Y	Y	B_K
G	R	R	G
W	W	W	W
G	R	R	G

W	B_L	W	B_K
W	W	B_K	B_K
B_K	B_K	W	W
B_K	W	B_L	W

PATTERN PAGE 5

G	G	W	W	G	G
G	G	W	W	G	G
B_K	B_K	R	R	B_K	B_K
Y	Y	R	R	Y	Y
B_K	B_K	R	R	B_K	B_K
G	G	W	W	G	G
G	G	W	W	G	G

86

PATTERN PAGE 6

R	B_L	W	R	B_L	W
R	B_L	W	R	B_L	W
R	B_L	W	R	B_L	W
R	B_L	W	R	B_L	W
R	B_L	W	R	B_L	W
R	B_L	W	R	B_L	W
R	B_L	W	R	B_L	W

PATTERN PAGE 7

R	R	R	R
R	B_L	B_L	B_L
R	B_L	G	G
R	B_L	G	W

B_K	W	B_K
B_K	B_K	B_K
B_K	W	B_K

G	B_L	R
B_L	B_L	R
R	R	R

Attribute Games and Activities
©1976, Creative Publications, Inc.

PATTERN PAGE 8

G	G	B_L	R
W	G	B_L	R
W	G	B_L	R
W	G	B_L	R
W	G	B_L	R

R	R	R
R	R	R
R	R	R

REPEATING DESIGNS

Materials: Color Cubes
Pattern Pages #1–4 (pages 82–85)
Graph Paper

Procedure: Ask students to think of each pattern as a rubber stamp. Using one stamp on the 6 x 6 graph paper, have them "print" the design over and over again. The only rule is the stamp must cover each 6 x 6 grid completely.

Further Teaching Suggestions:

An example of stamping is given on the next page. Try the same activity on 10 x 10 graph paper. What happens to the design at the edges?

This activity can be related to multiplication. For example, if this is the stamp used:

B_L	W
R	R

Ask:

"If the stamp was used one time, how many blue cubes would there be? If stamped two times, how many blue cubes would there be?"

"If stamped three times, how many blue cubes would there be?" The number of red cubes or white cubes might also be noted.

90

REPEATING A DESIGN

This is the stamp:

B_L	W	B_L
W	R	W

One way to stamp is:

B_L	W	B_L	B_L	W	B_L
W	R	W	W	R	W
B_L	W	B_L	B_L	W	B_L
W	R	W	W	R	W
B_L	W	B_L	B_L	W	B_L
W	R	W	W	R	W

Another way of stamping:
   Can you see how the
   stamp was used?

B_L	W	W	B_L	B_L	W
W	R	R	W	W	R
B_L	W	W	B_L	B_L	W
W	B_L	B_L	W	W	B_L
R	W	W	R	R	W
W	B_L	B_L	W	W	B_L

Use the same stamp to make
   a different design.

Attribute Games and Activities
©1976, Creative Publications, Inc.

ARRANGING THE CUBES

Make a design with Color Cubes that repeats in some way and covers the mat. Color your design.

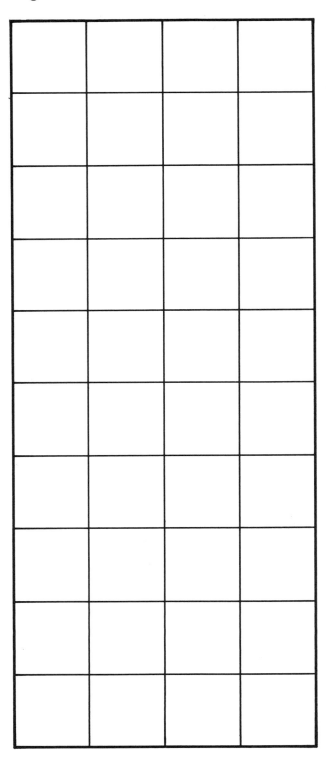

92

SOMEONE ELSE'S PATTERN

Can you see the pattern?

Cover the question marks with the cubes that fit the pattern. Now color the pattern.

B_L	Y	G	R	W	B_K
B_K	B_L	Y	G		
?					
	?				
?					

ANOTHER REPEATING DESIGN

Can you see the pattern?

Cover the question marks with the cubes that fit the pattern. Now color the pattern.

B_K	R	B_K	R	B_K	R
W	Y	W	Y	W	Y
B_K	R				
			Y	W	Y
			?		
			?	?	

Attribute Games and Activities
©1976, Creative Publications, Inc.

REPEATING DESIGN
3

Can you see the pattern?

B_K	W	W	B_K	W	W	B_K	W	W	B_K
W	W	B_K							
W	B_K								
					?	?			
					?	?			

Cover the question marks with the cubes that fit the pattern.

Attribute Games and Activities
©1976, Creative Publications, Inc.

MIRROR DESIGNS

Materials: Pattern Pages #1–8 (pages 82–89)
Piece of Yarn
Mirror

Procedure: Ask the students to choose a Pattern Page. Place a piece of yarn in a straight line to divide the design into two sections that might be folded to match. This line is called a **LINE OF SYMMETRY** of the design. Encourage the students to place a mirror on the line of symmetry to observe what happens. Examples of lines of symmetry are:

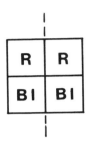 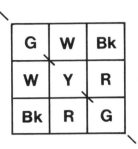

Another example is shown on page 97. Find the Pattern Page designs which have a line of symmetry.

Further Teaching Suggestions: As a follow-up activity, examine those Pattern Pages that have more than one line of symmetry. For example:

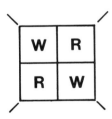

To extend the activity ask the students to create designs which have at least one line of symmetry. Students may then challenge other students to find the lines of symmetry in their designs.

AN EXAMPLE OF A SYMMETRIC DESIGN

B_L	W	B_L	W	B_L	W
B_K	R	B_K	R	B_K	R
B_L	W	B_L	W	B_L	W
B_L	W	B_L	W	B_L	W
B_K	R	B_K	R	B_K	R
B_L	W	B_L	W	B_L	W

line of symmetry ⎯ ⎯ ⎯ (between rows 3 and 4)

SUBSETS OF CUBES

Materials: Color Cubes
Two Loops

Procedure: Ask the students to place three different colored cubes in a loop. Then place a second loop within the first loop to make as many different groupings as possible. For example, starting with these blocks: R Bl W

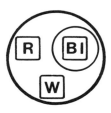 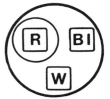 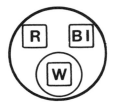 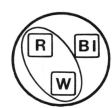

 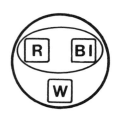  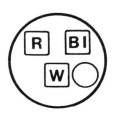

There are eight different ways the second loop may be placed within the first loop. Each set within the original set is called a SUBSET.

Further Teaching Suggestions: Pose the same question for other sets with various numbers of members. Record the results in a chart.

Number of blocks in set	Number of subsets
0	
1	
2	
3	8
4	
5	
6	
7	

Discuss any patterns that emerge.

98

MORE SUBSETS

Materials: Color Cubes

Procedure: Ask students to find the number of subsets possible for a set with a given number of members. Students should record the subsets in brackets. For example, the set of cubes $\{Bl, W, R\}$ has these subsets:

$$\{ \}, \{Bl\}, \{W\}, \{R\}, \{Bl, W\}, \{W, R\}, \{Bl, R\},$$
$$\{R, W, Bl\}$$

There are 8 subsets in all.
There is one subset with 0 members.
There are three subsets with 1 member.
There are three subsets with 2 members.
There is one subset with 3 members.

Further Teaching Suggestions: Ask students to investigate the number and kinds of subsets that may be formed for various sets. Record the kinds of subsets made on the worksheet.

Number of elements in set	Number of subsets having					
	0	1	2	3	4	5 members
0						
1						
2						
3	1	3	3	1	0	0
4						
5						

Discuss any patterns that emerge. A pattern may be more visible if the numbers in the chart are reorganized in a triangular arrangement

$$\begin{array}{ccccccc} & & & 1 & & & \\ & & 1 & & 1 & & \\ & 1 & & 2 & & 1 & \\ 1 & & 3 & & 3 & & 1 \end{array}$$

This triangular arrangement is an illustration of Pascal's Triangle.

HOW MANY WAYS?

Materials: Color Cubes

Procedure: Ask the students to take three cubes, each a different color. Have them arrange them in a row in as many different ways as possible. For example, if the cubes chosen were R, Bl and W 6 arrangements are possible.

| R | Bl | W | | Bl | W | R | | Bl | R | W | | W | Bl | R | | R | W | Bl | | W | R | Bl |

Take the number of colors indicated (one cube of each color) and find all the different ways to arrange them. Fill in the table.

Number of colors	Different arrangements (draw them)	Number of arrangements
1		
2		
3		6
4		
5		
6		

Discuss any pattern that emerges.

Further Teaching Suggestions: If n is the number of colors, the number of possible arrangements is n! (i.e., 1x2x 3x...xn). Thus, for 4 different colors the number of arrangements is 4x3x2x1 = 24. If students are going to find all arrangements, they must be guided to discover a systematic method for finding all the arrangements.

FOUR IN A ROW GAME

Materials: Color Cubes
10 x 10 Graph Paper

Procedure: This is a game for two players. Each player chooses one color of cubes as playing pieces. The first player places a piece anywhere on the graph paper. The second player places a piece so it touches one side or corner of the first piece.

Here are possible placements of the second cube:

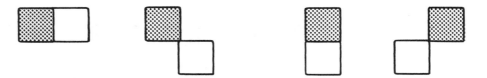

On the following turns, the only rule is that a new playing piece must touch one side or corner of a piece already on the graph paper.

The first person to have four playing pieces in a row wins. The row may be vertical, horizontal or diagonal.

Further Teaching Suggestions: An easier variation of this game is THREE IN A ROW. The rules are the same. However, the winner is the first player to place three playing pieces in a row.

MOVING PAIRS OF CUBES

Materials: Color Cubes
Pattern Page #9 (page 103)
10 x 10 Graph Paper

Procedure: Have the students cover the Pattern Page with the appropriate cubes. Ask the students to remove these two cubes | Y | G | from the pattern and to pretend that they are glued together to make a "log". The log is to be rotated 180° and replaced in the original design.

Demonstrate a rotation to the students. To rotate a log 180°, put the log on a piece of paper with a dot on the top. Then the piece of paper is turned so that the dot, which was at 12 o'clock, is at 6 o'clock.

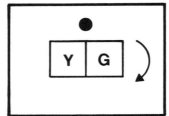 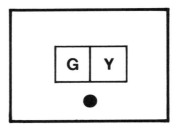

Replace each original log in the design with the rotated log. Record the new design on graph paper.

Further Teaching Suggestions: Ask the students to remove different horizontal pairs of cubes and rotate them 180°.

To extend the activity, ask students to remove more than two cubes at a time and rotate these longer "logs" 180°. Record these new designs on graph paper.

102

PATTERN PAGE 9

Y	G	Y	G	Y	G
B_L	W	B_L	W	B_L	W
Y	G	Y	G	Y	G
B_L	W	B_L	W	B_L	W
Y	G	Y	G	Y	G
B_L	W	B_L	W	B_L	W

ROTATING LOGS

Materials: Color Cubes
Pattern Page #9 (page 103)
6×6 Graph Paper

Procedure: Ask students to cover the Pattern Page with the appropriate cubes. Choose two cubes that would make a vertical log. Pretend the vertical log is made of these two cubes glued together. Students rotate the vertical log 180° and replace it in the design each time it appears. For example,

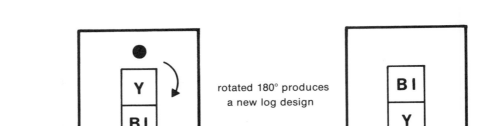

Each time [log] appears in the original design it is replaced with the rotated version [log] Have students record the new design on graph paper.

104

MORE MOVES

Materials: Color Cubes
Pattern Page #9 (page 103)
10 x 10 Graph Paper

Procedure: Choose a square of four cubes in the pattern. Ask students to imagine that the four cubes are glued together. Every time the square appears in the design it is replaced with a new version which has been rotated 180°. Demonstrate the rotation to students.

rotated 180° produces

Ask students to record the new design on graph paper.

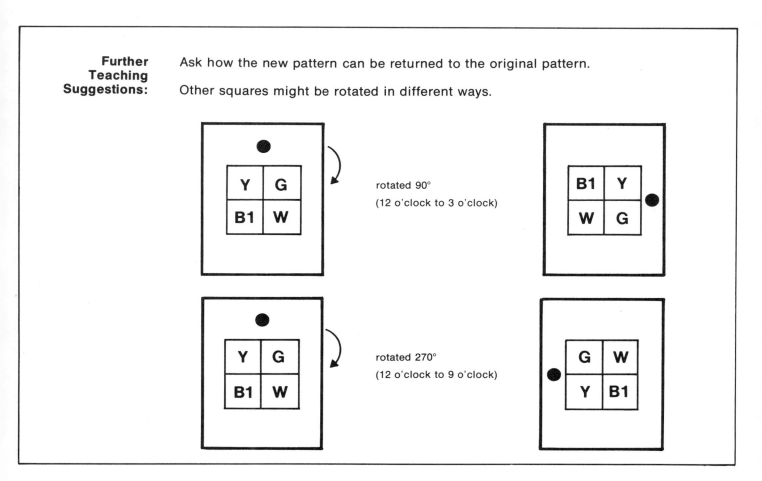

Further Teaching Suggestions: Ask how the new pattern can be returned to the original pattern.

Other squares might be rotated in different ways.

rotated 90°
(12 o'clock to 3 o'clock)

rotated 270°
(12 o'clock to 9 o'clock)

FLIPPING LOGS

Materials: Color Cubes
Pattern Page #9 (page 103)
10 x 10 Graph Paper

Procedure: Ask the students to cover the Pattern Page with the appropriate cubes. Choose a log of two cubes and ask the students to imagine that the cubes are glued together.

Demonstrate the log being flipped around a horizontal line. For example,

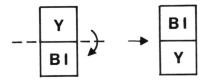

Ask the students to replace the original log with its flipped version each time it appears on the Pattern Page. Record the new design on graph paper. Other flips may be considered.

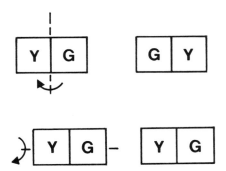

Further Teaching Suggestions: "Flipping" designs may be related to lines of symmetry. If a design is flipped about a line of symmetry, the design is unchanged. For example:

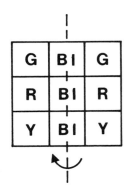

106

FLIPPING GROUPS OF CUBES

Materials: Color Cubes
Pattern Page #9 (page 103)
10 x 10 Graph Paper

Procedure: Ask the students to cover the Pattern Page with the appropriate cubes. Choose a square of four cubes and ask the students to imagine they are glued together. Demonstrate the square being flipped around a vertical line. For example,

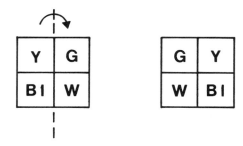

Ask the students to replace the original square with its flipped version each time it occurs in the design. Record the new design on graph paper.

Further Teaching Suggestions: To extend the activity, use other Pattern Pages and other squares.

107

MORE FLIPS

Materials: Color Cubes
Pattern Page #9 (page 103)
10 x 10 Graph Paper

Procedure: Ask the students to cover the design with the appropriate cubes. Have them consider a square of four cubes and imagine that the four cubes are glued together. Each time the square appears in the design it is to be replaced by the square which has been flipped along its horizontal axis. For example,

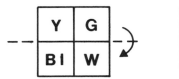

Ask students to record the new design on graph paper.

Further Teaching Suggestions: To extend this activity, the square might be flipped along a diagonal axis and the result placed in the original design.

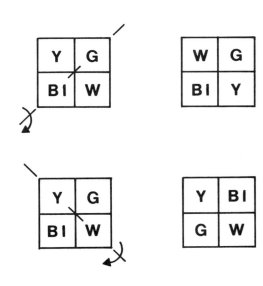

108

COMBINING MOVES

Materials: Color Cubes
Pattern Page #9 (page 103)
10 x 10 Graph Paper

Procedure: Ask students to cover the design with the appropriate cubes. Choose a square arrangement of four cubes. This square will be moved twice before it is replaced in the design. For example,

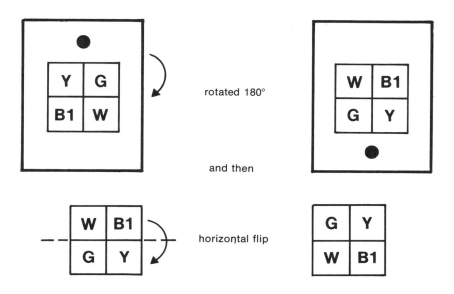

Each time the square occurs in the design it is replaced with the new version. Record the new design on graph paper.

Students may work with various Pattern Pages, removing squares and creating new designs.

Further Teaching Suggestions: Some interesting questions to consider include:

"Does it matter if the square is flipped horizontally first and then turned 180°?"

"Could the square be moved only once and have the same effect as the two moves described?"

To extend the activity, try other combinations of moves, such as a 90° turn and a vertical flip; a 90° turn and a 270° turn; a horizontal flip and a 270° turn, etc.

EXTENSIONS TO NUMBERS

EXTENSIONS TO NUMBERS

The concepts of sets, subset, unions and intersections are extended in this section to the study of sets of numbers; in particular we will consider the numbers 1–100, as they appear in the Hundred Chart. The activities show how set concepts which were developed during experiences with the Attribute Materials can be extended to more abstract numerical work.

A Hundred Chart and Color Cubes or the Hundred Chart mounted on cardboard and cut into individual number tiles are the physical materials that will be used in this section. The students manipulate numeral "tiles" to help them prepare for the abstraction of numbers.

1	2	3	4	5	6	7	8	9	10
11	12	13	14	15	16	17	18	19	20
21	22	23	24	25	26	27	28	29	30
31	32	33	34	35	36	37	38	39	40
41	42	43	44	45	46	47	48	49	50
51	52	53	54	55	56	57	58	59	60
61	62	63	64	65	66	67	68	69	70
71	72	73	74	75	76	77	78	79	80
81	82	83	84	85	86	87	88	89	90
91	92	93	94	95	96	97	98	99	100

Hundred Chart

Hundred Mat

33   7   95   60   66   1

Individual Number Tiles

Color Cubes

If the activities are used with younger students, or less advanced older students, the numbers may be limited to one to twenty-five or one through fifty. For these students, interlocking cubes, such as Unifix, may be used in place of the Color Cubes since they are not as easily disturbed when arranged.

112

ARRANGING THE NUMERALS

Materials: Number Tiles (mounted on cardboard and cut from the Hundred Chart)
Hundred Mat

Procedure: Ask the students to arrange the tiles according to a particular rule or pattern. For example, put the numbers on the Hundred Mat in order from smallest to largest.

1	2	3	4	5	6	7	8	9	10
11	12								

Hold the 5 x 10 Arrangement Mat so there are five tiles across. Put the number tiles in order from smallest to largest.

1	2	3	4	5
6	7			

Use the 3 x 10 Arrangement Mat. Hold the mat so there are three tiles across. Put the number tiles in order from smallest to largest. Have students choose other arrangement mats and see if they can make predictions and continue the patterns given.

Further Teaching Suggestions: Ask students to look for patterns after the number tiles have been arranged.

Ask where 112 would be placed if each mat were extended.

HUNDRED CHART

1	2	3	4	5	6	7	8	9	10
11	12	13	14	15	16	17	18	19	20
21	22	23	24	25	26	27	28	29	30
31	32	33	34	35	36	37	38	39	40
41	42	43	44	45	46	47	48	49	50
51	52	53	54	55	56	57	58	59	60
61	62	63	64	65	66	67	68	69	70
71	72	73	74	75	76	77	78	79	80
81	82	83	84	85	86	87	88	89	90
91	92	93	94	95	96	97	98	99	100

Attribute Games and Activities
©1976, Creative Publications, Inc

HUNDRED MAT

5 x 10 ARRANGEMENT MAT

Attribute Games and Activities
©1976, Creative Publications, Inc.

3 x 10 ARRANGEMENT MAT

ANOTHER ARRANGEMENT

100	99	98	97	96	95	94	93	92	91
90	89								

What pattern do you see for this arrangment of tiles? Can you predict where 63 will fall on the mat? Which column? Which Row? Continue the pattern.

Attribute Games and Activities
©1976, Creative Publications, Inc.

ARRANGING THE TILES

What is the pattern?
Predict where these tiles would fall on this mat. | 43 | | 67 |
Continue placing the tiles.

1	3	5	7	9
11	13			

Attribute Games and Activities
©1976, Creative Publications, Inc.

A DIFFERENT ARRANGEMENT

Find and continue the pattern.

2	4	6	8	10
12	14			

Predict where ⬜31 , ⬜62 , ⬜80 will be placed.

Attribute Games and Activities
©1976, Creative Publications, Inc.

CHALLENGE ARRANGEMENT

Find and continue the pattern.

1	2	3	5	8
13	21	34		

SORTING THE NUMERALS

Materials: Hundred Chart
Color Cubes

Procedure: Ask the students to use the cubes on the Hundred Chart to cover particular sets of numbers that you describe. For example, numbers whose last digit is 7. After the first few numbers have been covered, ask students to look for a pattern and place more blocks accordingly.

Now try these:
Numbers whose first digit is 3.
Numbers whose last digit is less than 5.
Numbers whose first and last digits are less than 3.
Numbers whose last digit is more than 9 and whose first digit is more than 8.
Numbers whose first digit is less than 4 or whose last digit is less than 2.
Numbers the sum of whose digits is 9. (Why does this pattern occur?)
Numbers the sum of whose digits is 11.

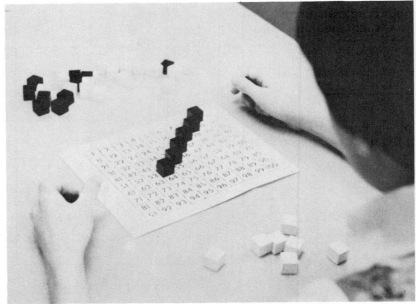

Further Teaching Suggestions: To extend this activity, describe some not-sets. For example, numbers not having 3 as a digit.

122

FINDING MULTIPLES

Materials: Hundred Chart
Color Cubes (several sets)

Procedure: Ask the students to choose Color Cubes of one color and cover all the multiples of a particular number on the Hundred Chart. For example, cover the multiples of 5.

1	2	3	4		6	7	8	9	
11	12	13	14		16	17	18	19	
21	22	23	24		26	27	28	29	
31	32	33	34		36	37	38	39	

After the students have placed a few cubes, ask them to look for a pattern and place more cubes accordingly.

After all the multiples of 5 are covered, ask the students to remove each cube and say the number aloud. Record the numbers that are read. Try covering other multiples.

Further Teaching Suggestions: If the students do not know the meaning of multiple, they may simply count off. For example, to find the multiples of 4, count by fours. At each count of 4 a Color Cube is placed on the chart.

one	two	three	four	one	two	three	four	one	two
1	2	3		5	6	7		9	10
11		13	14	15		17	18	19	
three	four	one	two	three	four	one	two	three	four

123

COMMON MULTIPLES

Materials: Hundred Chart
Color Cubes (several sets)

Procedure: Ask students to choose Color Cubes of one color and to cover all the multiples of a given number. All the cubes are left in place. Now ask the students to choose cubes of a different color and to cover the multiples of another number. Some squares will have a tower of two cubes on them. The number under its towers is called a **COMMON MULTIPLE** of the two numbers represented by the tower.

Ask the students to find the common multiples of various pairs of numbers by placing cubes on their multiples on the Hundred Chart.

Further Teaching Suggestions: An example of finding the common multiples of 2 and 7 is given on the next page.

Pose exploratory questions such as:

"Are all the multiples of 2 also multiples of 6?"

"What are the common multiples of 3 and 4?"

"Look at the common multiples of 5 and 3."

"Is there another way to describe these numbers?"

"What is the smallest (least) common multiple of 3 and 4?"

Try finding common multiples of three numbers using three different colors of cubes.

MULTIPLES OF 2 BLUE   MULTIPLES OF 7 RED

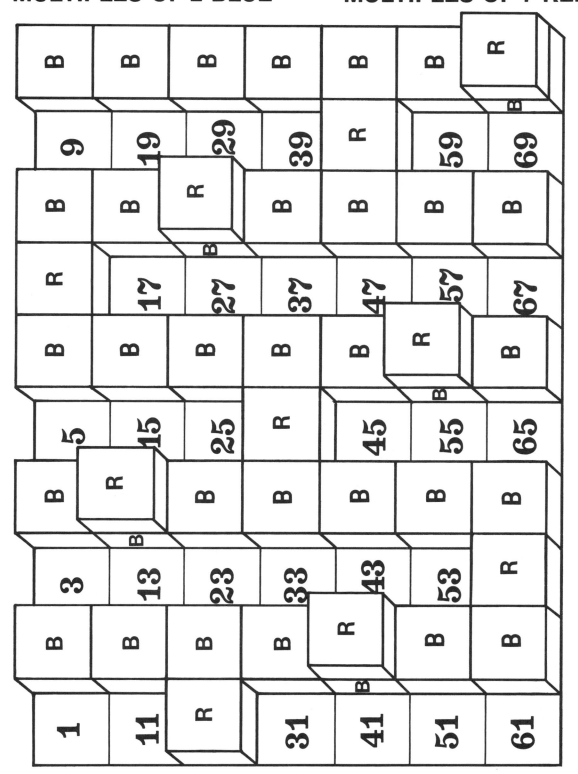

MAKING WINDOWS

Materials: Hundred Mats
Hundred Chart
Color Cubes
Scissors

Procedure: After a pattern for a multiple has been found, a window* may be made. Ask the students to find the multiples of a particular number. Each multiple is covered by a cube. For example, multiples of 6:

1	2	3	4	5	░	7	8	9	10
11	░	13	14	15	16	17	░	19	20
21	22	23	░	25	26	27	28	29	░

Ask the students to take a blank Hundred Mat and cut out those squares on which a cube would be placed. When this window is placed over the Hundred Chart, only the multiples of 6 show through.

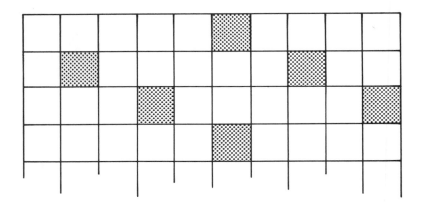

<table>
<tbody><tr><td></td><td></td><td></td><td></td><td></td><td>░</td><td></td><td></td><td></td><td></td></tr>
<tr><td></td><td>░</td><td></td><td></td><td></td><td></td><td></td><td>░</td><td></td><td></td></tr>
<tr><td></td><td></td><td></td><td>░</td><td></td><td></td><td></td><td></td><td></td><td>░</td></tr>
<tr><td></td><td></td><td></td><td></td><td>░</td><td></td><td></td><td></td><td></td><td></td></tr></tbody></table>

Further Teaching Suggestions:	After windows have been made for several different multiples, ask the students to place two windows over the Hundred Chart at the same time. Observe the numbers that show through. For example, if the 3-window and the 2-window were placed on the Hundred Chart, common multiples of these two numbers would show through. Patterns for various windows are on the following pages.

*Nuffield Mathematics Project is the source of ''windows.''

126

2-WINDOW

Cut out shaded areas.

3-WINDOW

5-WINDOW

7-WINDOW

Attribute Games and Activities
©1976, Creative Publications, Inc.

INVESTIGATING WINDOW PATTERNS

Materials: Hundred Chart
                   Windows for Various Multiples

Procedure: After the students have made several windows, some interesting questions might
                   be posed. Have the students place two windows over the Hundred Chart at the same
                   time. Observe the numbers that show through. For example, if the 3-window and the
                   2-window were placed on the Hundred Chart, these numbers would show through.

				6				
12					18			
		24						30
			36					
42					48			

Does it matter in which order the two windows are placed on the Hundred Chart?

Further Teaching Suggestions: If only 2-, 3-, 5-, 7-windows were provided, could you get the multiples of 4 to show?
The multiples of 10?

COVERING THE CHART

Materials: Hundred Chart
Color Cubes (Several sets are required; if not available, squares of colored paper may be used.)

Procedure: Ask the students to cover all the multiples of 2 with one color, then all the multiples of 3 with another color. Cover all the multiples of 4 with another color and so on until the multiples of 2 through 10 are each covered with a cube of a different color. Several different kinds of towers should emerge.

Further Teaching Suggestions: Ask questions such as:

"Which number has the highest tower?"

"Which numbers have the lowest towers?"

Find the multiples that are covered by more than 3 cubes. Notice that multiples of 1 are not considered. Every number is a multiple of 1.

COMMON FACTORS

Materials: Hundred Chart
Color Cubes (several sets)

Procedure: Ask the students to cover the Hundred Chart with cubes as was done on page 132. Introduce the concept of factor. If the number 12 is covered by cubes for multiples of 2, 3, 4 and 6, then 2, 3, 4 and 6 are called **FACTORS** of 12. If the number 15 is covered by cubes for multiples of 3 and 5, then 3 and 5 are factors of 15.

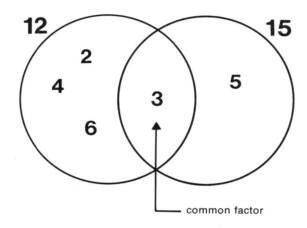

common factor

The loops show that the number 3 is a **COMMON FACTOR** of both 12 and 15 because the 3 falls in the intersection of the two loops.

Ask students to find the factors of other numbers and to look for other common factors.

Further Teaching Suggestions: Similarly, 15 is a common multiple of the numbers 3 and 5. Pose questions such as:

"What is the largest (greatest) factor of 20 shown by the cubes?"

"What factor is common to both 15 and 21?"

"What is the greatest common factor of 12 and 20?"

PRIME NUMBERS

Materials: Hundred Chart
Colored Pencils or Crayons
2, 3, 5 and 7 Windows

Procedure: Students can isolate the Prime Numbers less than 100 on their Hundred Chart using a method called the Sieve of Eratosthenes. A Prime Number is a natural number which has exactly two factors, itself and one:
3 is prime, 1 x 3
5 is prime, 1 x 5
4 is composite (not prime), 1 x 4, 2 x 2
6 is composite, 1 x 6, 2 x 3.

The number **one** is neither prime nor composite; mathematicians have agreed that since one only has itself as a factor, it is unique.

Have students do the following on their Hundred Chart:
(1) Cross out 1 because it is a special number.
(2) With a colored pencil circle the 2 (because it is prime). Place the 2-window on the Hundred Chart and draw slanted lines through all multiples of 2.
(3) Using a different color for each number, proceed as in step (2) above for the numbers 3, 5 and 7.
(4) Circle all remaining numbers which have not been crossed out.

Further Teaching Suggestions: Do we need to cross out the multiples of 4, 6, 8 and 9?

Have students make a list of the numbers circled on their Hundred Chart. These are the Prime Numbers less than 100.

FINDING THE LEAST COMMON MULTIPLE AND THE GREATEST COMMON FACTOR USING LOOPS

Materials: None

Procedure: Find the LEAST COMMON MULTIPLE (LCM) and GREATEST COMMON FACTOR (GCF) of 30 and 42. First, ask the students to find the prime factorization of each number. One suggested method follows:

(The prime factors of 30.)   (The prime factors of 42.)

Each prime number is considered a separate factor. The set of prime factors for 30 are 2, 3, 5. The set of prime factors for 42 are 2, 3, 7. Draw a loop diagram and place the factors as follows:

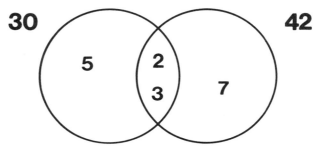

The 2 and 3 in the intersection are common factors of 30 and 42. The **GREATEST COMMON FACTOR** is 2 x 3 = 6. The **LEAST COMMON MULTIPLE** is the product of the factor which comprise the union of the two sets; 2 x 3 x 5 x 7 = 210.

Find the GCF and LCM of 36 and 24.

$$36 = 2 \times 2 \times 3 \times 3$$
$$24 = 2 \times 2 \times 2 \times 3$$

GCF = 2 x 2 x 3 = 12; LCM = 2 x 2 x 2 x 3 x 3 = 72.

Try a few more problems with the students.

Further Teaching Suggestions: If a factor appears more than once in the same number, each is listed among the set of factors for each number.

Try problems involving three numbers and three overlapping loops.

Student Activity Pages (pages 136–138) include problems using two and three loops.

FINDING LCM AND GCF

Factor each number.
Arrange the factors in a Venn diagram.
Find the LCM and GCF.

∩ = intersection   U = union

		Venn diagram	GCF A∩B	LCM AUB
1	A = 54, B = 72 A = 3 x 3 x 3 x 2 B = 3 x 3 x 2 x 2 x 2	A (3) (3 3 2) (2 2) B	GCF = 3 x 3 x 2 = 18	LCM = 3 x 3 x 3 x 2 x 2 x 2 = 216
2	A = 21, B = 84			
3	A = 26, B = 39			
4	A = 147, B = 98			

Attribute Games and Activities
©1976, Creative Publications, Inc.

MORE LCM's AND GCF's

Factor each number.
Arrange the factors in a Venn diagram.
Find the LCM and GCF.

		Venn diagram	GCF $A \cap B \cap C$	LCM $A \cup B \cup C$
1	A = 75, B = 72, C = 60 A = 5 x 5 x 3 B = 3 x 3 x 2 x 2 x 2 C = 5 x 2 x 2 x 3	A: 5, B: 3, 2, center 3, 2, 2, C: 5, 2	GCF = 3	LCM = 5 x 5 x 3 x 3 x 2 x 2 x 2 = 1800
2	A = 100, B = 30, C = 45			
3	A = 50, B = 70, C = 18			
4	A = 12, B = 27, C = 42			

REVIEWING LCM AND GCF

Factor each number.
Arrange the factors in a Venn Diagram.
Find the LCM and GCF.

		Venn diagram	GCF	LCM
1	A = 36, B = 60			
2	A = 14, B = 84, C = 5			
3	A = 50, B = 24			
4	A = 40, B = 12, C = 56			

Attribute Games and Activities
©1976, Creative Publications, Inc.

PROBLEM SOLVING USING SETS

Materials: Problems to Solve Page

Procedure: Pose problems such as:
In a recent survey, of 378 people who ate cereal for breakfast, 63 also had fruit for breakfast. 588 ate either fruit or cereal. How many people eat only fruit?

Explain that the key elements are not the particular people in each set, but the number of people there are falling in certain categories. The first task is to find the specific sets involved.

In this problem, Set A = people who ate cereal and Set B = people who ate fruit. Next list the information given in the problem. Number in Set A = 378. Number in $A \cap B = 63$. Number in $A \cup B = 588$. Draw a Venn diagram and record the numerical information on it.

Since Set A has 378 members and $A \cap B$ has 63 members, $378 - 63 = 315$.

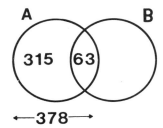

Since Set A has 378 members and $A \cup B$ has 588 members, $588 - 378 = 210$.

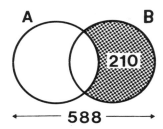

The shaded area includes the people in Set B but not in Set A. That is, the people who ate fruit but not cereal.

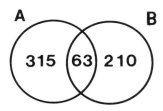

Ask students to do other problems in a similar manner.

PROBLEMS TO SOLVE

EXAMPLE:
During the winter vacation it snowed on 13 days, sleeted on 17 days and rained on 10 days. On 3 days it rained and sleeted and snowed. (It was miserable!!!) On 4 days it sleeted and snowed. On 5 days it sleeted and rained. On 8 days it rained and snowed. On how many days was the weather inclement (i.e., rained or sleeted or snowed)?

The solution is the number of days in the union of the 3 sets. To determine this union we must:

(1) Draw the loops and label them as shown. (There are 3 loops because there are 3 types of inclement weather.) Since it "rained *and* sleeted *and* snowed" for 3 days, a "3" is placed in the intersection of all 3 loops.

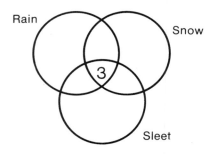

(2) Since "on 4 days it sleeted *and* snowed" we need to show one additional day in the snow-sleet intersection for a total of 4 days, i.e., 3 + 1 = 4.
Similarly, since it sleeted and rained on a total of 5 days, we conclude that it sleeted and rained (but did not snow) on 2 days, i.e., 3 + 2 = 5. Also, it must have rained and snowed (but not sleeted) on 5 days, i.e., 3 + 5 = 8.

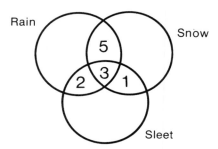

(3) We know that it snowed on a total of 13 days. On 9 (1 + 3 + 5 = 9) of those days it also rained *or* sleeted. Therefore, it only snowed on 4 days (13 − 9 = 4). Similarly, we can determine the number of days on which it *only* rained or *only* sleeted.

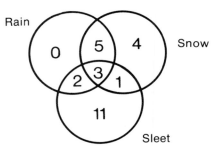

(4) To determine the number of days on which the weather was inclement (the union of the 3 sets), add the number of elements in each region of the diagram (0 + 5 + 4 + 2 + 3 + 1 + 11 = 26).

Attribute Games and Activities
©1976, Creative Publications, Inc.

PROBLEMS TO SOLVE

1. John and Joe owned 4 dogs jointly. John owned 3 himself. Altogether they had 12 dogs in the kennel. How many did each have?

2. Tony had taken 10 business trips during the year. On 4 trips he went to both New York and Washington. On 3 trips he went to New York only. Tony went only to New York and Washington. How often did he go to Washington? To New York?

3. In Newton, in a particular neighborhood, 20 people cheered for the Celtics, 40 cheered for the Bruins and 7 cheered for both. How many cheered for neither if there are 55 people in the neighborhood?

4. A vending machine selling Coke and Root Beer sold only 49 bottles of soda on a particular day. Twenty-seven people bought Coke. 30 people bought Root Beer. How many bought both?

5. On a test 112 A's were given. This was the total number of A's for both parts of the test. The test had two sections. On the first section 42 people received A. On the second section 91 people received A. How many people received A on both sections?

6. A local garden club has 60 women, 23 bought gladiolas only. 26 bought tulip bulbs only. Some bought neither. Four bought both. How many bought neither?

7. Tom's class had been questioned on which subjects they liked and disliked. The results were as follows: 18 liked mathematics, 32 liked English, and 25 liked languages. 16 said they liked both English and languages, but only 7 said they liked both mathematics and English. Only 3 said they liked all three subjects and none admitted that he did not like any subject. How many children are in Tom's class if 9 students liked math and languages?

8. In a survey about the popularity of cars, 200 people were questioned. 25 people only owned Fords, 40 people owned both Chevrolets and Oldsmobiles, 15 people had owned Fords and Chevrolets. 10 people liked and owned all three makes. 70 people owned Chevrolets and 25 people owned only Chevrolets. How many owned Oldsmobiles?

9. A math teacher conducted a survey in her classes. 42 students chewed gum in class; 55 talked incessantly; and 25 fell asleep during class. Four people both talked and fell asleep but didn't chew gum. Six students fell asleep and chewed gum, but at least didn't talk. Forty students only talked. Ten students talked and chewed gum, but didn't fall asleep. How many students were there in all? How many students talked and chewed gum and slept (UGH)?

10. In the 7th grade there were 90 students. 38 received an A in math. 12 received an A in English and math, but not in social studies. 14 received only an A in English. 8 received an A in social studies and math but not in English. 9 received an A in social studies and English but not in math. 7 received an A in math only. How many received an A in English? In all three subjects? Only in social studies?

11. A panel of sports writers was rating various hockey teams. Four writers rated Teams I, II and III as tied for tops. Nine writers rated Teams I and II as tops. 11 writers ranked Teams II and III as tops and 6 rated only Team I as tops. In all there were 75 writers polled. 26 favored Team I as tops while 30 favored Team II as tops. How many favored Team III as tops?

Attribute Games and Activities
©1976, Creative Publications, Inc.

APPENDIX

Directions for Making:

ATTRIBUTE PLAYING CARDS

Materials: Blank playing cards or 3 x 5 index cards
Felt tip pens (black, red, green, yellow, blue)
Attribute Blocks
Scissors

Procedure: This deck of Attribute Playing Cards is for use in the Attribute Card Game on page 19 of Attribute Games and Activities. A deck consists of 40 cards; four each of the 10 values for the Attribute Blocks: red, yellow, green, blue; circle, square, triangle, diamond; large, small. For younger students, an agreed upon symbol for large and small, with or without the words may be desirable. Otherwise, only the words need appear. So that the "symbols" show on the cards when held in the hand fan fashion, try a layout similar to the following.

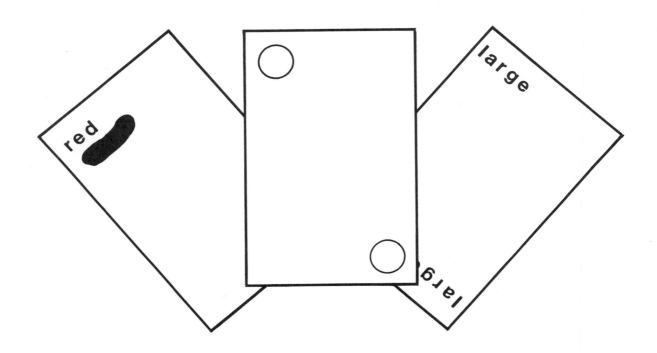

Use: In addition to the Attribute Card Game, the teacher and students can create their own card games using this deck and similar decks with the other components of ATTRIBUTE GAMES AND PROBLEMS materials.

Attribute Games and Activities
©1976, Creative Publications, Inc.

SOLUTIONS

ATTRIBUTE GAMES AND ACTIVITIES

Page 21. Someone Else's Arrangement

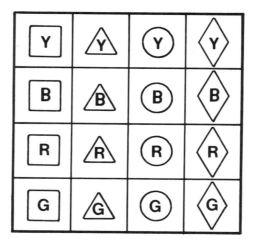

Stack small blocks on top of large blocks.
Place small blocks below or to the right of large blocks.

Page 24. Who Am I? Game

(1) Large, red square
(2) Small, red circle
(3) Large, green diamond
(4) Small, green circle

Page 32. A Three-Difference Train

One solution is:

Yes.

Page 36. What Is Missing in the Two-Difference "H"?

One solution is: Challenge question:

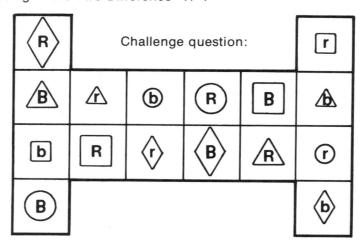

145

Page 38. What is Missing in the Square?

One solution is:

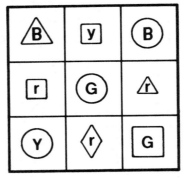

Yes
Many solutions are possible.

Page 39. 4 x 4 Arranging Mat

Two-difference square using only large blocks.

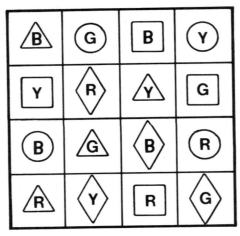

Yes

Page 40. What Is Missing in the Square?

One solution is:

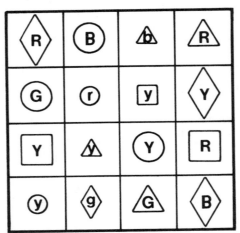

Yes
Yes

146

Pages 41. Watch It! Game

Arrangement using only large blocks.

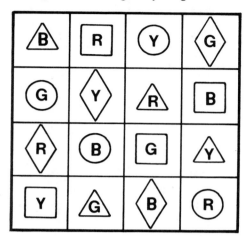

Page 53. Three-Loop Problems.

A - small, red, not-square
B - small, red, square
C - small, not-red, square
D - large, red, not-square
E - large, red, square
F - large, not-red, square
G - large, not-red, not-square

Page 56. Detective Questions

1. △r □r ○r ◇r

2. △r

3. 16
4. 3
5. 23
6. 20
7. 8

8. △y △b △q

9. ◇R ○R □R ◇r ○r □r □g ○g ◇g ◇b ○b □b □y ○y ◇y

10. ◇r □r ○r

147

Page 61. Someone Else's Arrangement

Page 66. Special Arrangements

148

Page 74. Missing Persons

1. red, thin, female, child
2. blue, fat, female, adult
3. blue, thin, male, child

Page 75. Three-Loop Problems

A - fat, male, child
B - fat, female, child
C - thin, female, child
D - fat, male, adult
E - fat, female, adult
F - thin, female, adult
G - thin, male, adult

Page 93. Someone Else's Pattern

Bl	Y	G	R	W	Bk
Bk	Bl	Y	G	R	W
W	Bk	Bl	Y	G	R
R	W	Bk	Bl	Y	G
G	R	W	Bk	Bl	Y
Y	G	R	W	Bk	Bl

Page 94. Another Repeating Design

Bk	R	Bk	R	Bk	R
W	Y	W	Y	W	Y
Bk	R	Bk	R	Bk	R
W	Y	W	Y	W	Y
Bk	R	Bk	R	Bk	R
W	Y	W	Y	W	Y
Bk	R	Bk	R	Bk	R

Page 95. Repeating Design—3

square of question marks only

W	W
W	Bk

Page 98. Subsets of Cubes

Number of Blocks in Set	Number of Subsets
0	1
1	2
2	4
3	8
n	2^n

Page 102. Moving Pairs of Cubes

Since more than one solution is possible, students are
encouraged to check each other's responses.

Page 121. Challenge Arrangement

1	2	3	5	8
13	21	34	55	89
144	233	377		

A number is the sum of the 2 preceeding numbers, i.e.,
$34 = 13 + 21$, $55 = 21 + 34$.

Page 122. Sorting the Numerals

Numbers whose last digit is 7: seventh column
Numbers whose first digit is 3: fourth row
Numbers whose last digit is less than 5: first four columns
Numbers whose first and last digit is less than 3:
Numbers whose last digit is more than 9: none
Numbers whose first digit is more than 8: tenth row
Numbers whose first digit is less than 4 or whose last digit is less than 2:
Numbers the sum of whose digits is 6:
Numbers the sum of whose digits is 9:
Numbers the sum of whose digits is 11:

Page 136. Finding LCM and GCF

2. $A = 21 = 3 \times 7$, $B = 84 = 2 \times 2 \times 3 \times 7$

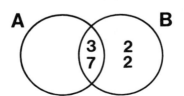

GCF $= 3 \times 7 = 21$
LCM $= 3 \times 7 \times 2 \times 2 = 84$

150

3. A = 26 = 2 × 13, B = 39 = 3 × 13

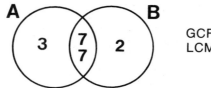

GCF = 13
LCM = 2 × 3 × 13 = 78

4. A = 147 = 3 × 7 × 7, B = 98 = 2 × 7 × 7

GCF = 7 × 7 = 49
LCM = 7 × 7 × 3 × 2 = 294

Page 137. More LCM's and GCF's

2. A = 100 = 2 × 2 × 5 × 5, B = 30 = 2 × 3 × 5, C = 45 = 5 × 3 × 3

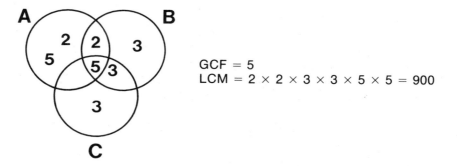

GCF = 5
LCM = 2 × 2 × 3 × 3 × 5 × 5 = 900

3. A = 50 = 2 × 5 × 5, B = 70 = 2 × 5 × 7, C = 18 = 2 × 3 × 3

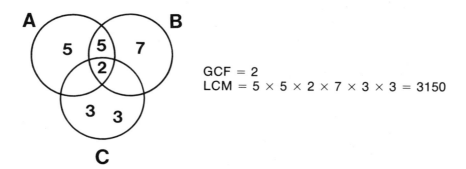

GCF = 2
LCM = 5 × 5 × 2 × 7 × 3 × 3 = 3150

151

4. A = 12 = 2 × 2 × 3, B = 27 = 3 × 3 × 3, C = 42 = 7 × 3 × 2

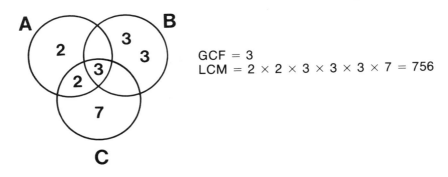

GCF = 3
LCM = 2 × 2 × 3 × 3 × 3 × 7 = 756

Page 138. Reviewing LCM and GCF

1. A = 36 = 2 × 2 × 3 × 3, B = 60 = 2 × 2 × 3 × 5

GCF = 2 × 2 × 3 = 12
LCM = 2 × 2 × 3 × 3 × 5 = 180

2. A = 14 = 2 × 7, B = 84 = 2 × 2 × 3 × 7, C = 5

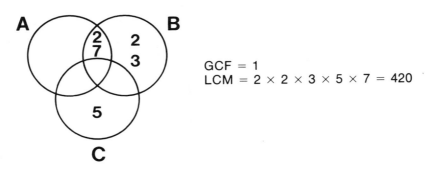

GCF = 1
LCM = 2 × 2 × 3 × 5 × 7 = 420

3. A = 50 = 2 × 5 × 5, B = 24 = 2 × 2 × 2 × 3

GCF = 2
LCM = 2 × 2 × 2 × 3 × 5 × 5 = 600

152

4. A = 40 = 2 × 2 × 2 × 5, B = 12 = 2 × 2 × 3, C = 56 = 2 × 2 × 2 × 7

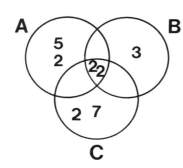

GCF = 2 × 2 = 4
LCM = 2 × 2 × 2 × 2 × 3 × 5 × 7 = 1680

Page 141. Problems to Solve

1. John owned 7 dogs and Joe owned 9 dogs.

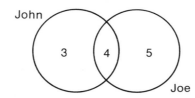

2. Seven trips to New York and seven trips to Washington.

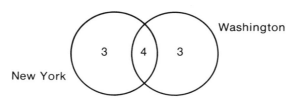

3. Two did not cheer.

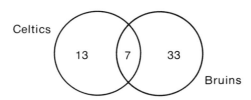

4. Eight bought both.

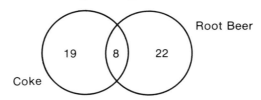

5. 21 received A on both sections.

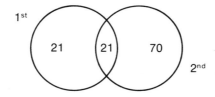

153

6. Seven bought neither.

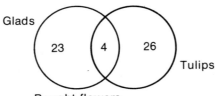

Bought flowers
$23 + 4 + 26 = 53$
$60 - 53 = 7$ bought none.

7. Tom's class has 46 students.

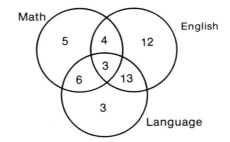

8. Oldsmobiles were owned by 145 people.

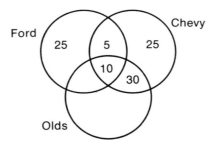

$25 + 5 + 25 = 55$ never owned oldsmobiles, $200 - 55 = 145$ owned oldsmobiles.

9. Only one talked and chewed gum and slept.

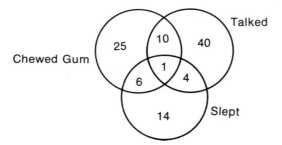

154

10. 46 received A in English, 11 in all three and 29 only in social studies.

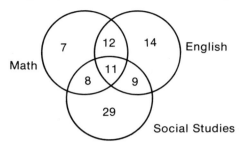

11. Team III was favored as tops by 50 writers.

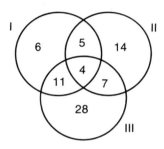